Nelson *Mathematics* 7

Teacher's Resource

Chapter 10: 3-D Geometry

Series Authors and Senior Consultants
Marian Small • Mary Lou Kestell

Senior Author
David Zimmer

Authors
Bernard A. Beales • Maria Bodiam • Doug Duff • Robin Foster • Cathy Hall • Jack Hope
Chris Kirkpatrick • Beata Kroll Myhill • Geoff Suderman-Gladwell • Joyce Tonner

Teacher's Resource Chapter Author
Margaret E. Curto

Assessment Consultant
Damian Cooper

THOMSON

NELSON

Australia   Canada   Mexico   Singapore   Spain   United Kingdom   United States

THOMSON

NELSON

**Nelson Mathematics 7
Teacher's Resource**

Series Consultants
Marian Small, Mary Lou Kestell

Senior Author
David Zimmer

Director of Publishing
Beverley Buxton

Publisher, Mathematics
Colin Garnham

Managing Editor, Development
David Spiegel

Senior Program Manager
Shirley Barrett

Program Manager
Tony Rodrigues

**Teacher's Resource
Program Manager**
Alan Simpson

Developmental Editors
Janis Barr, Julie Bedford,
Anna Garnham, Adrienne Mason,
Margaret McClintock, Tom Shields,
Robert Templeton, First Folio
Resource Group

Teacher's Resource Authors
Kaye Appleby, Anne Cirillo,
Donna Commerford, Lynda Cowan,
Marg Curto, Wendy Klassen,
Margret McClintlock, Susan Stuart,
Rosita Tseng-Tam, Mary Steele

Editorial Assistant
Megan Robinson

**Executive Managing Editor,
Production**
Nicola Balfour

**Executive Managing Editor,
Special Projects**
Cheryl Turner

Production Editor
Susan Selby

Proofreader
Tilman Lewis

Senior Production Coordinator
Sharon Latta Paterson

Production Coordinator
Franca Mandarino

Creative Director
Angela Cluer

Art Director
Ken Phipps

Assessment Consultant
Damian Cooper

Art Management
ArtPlus Ltd.

Illustrators
ArtPlus Ltd.

Interior and Cover Design
Suzanne Peden

Cover Image
Martin Barraud/Stone/Getty Images

**ArtPlus Ltd. Production
Coordinator**
Dana Lloyd

Compositor
ArtPlus Ltd.

Permissions
Vicki Gould

Printer
Webcom Ltd.

**Library and Archives Canada
Cataloguing in Publication**

Nelson mathematics 7.
Teacher's resource /
Marian Small ... [et al.].

Includes 14 booklets.
ISBN 0-17-626913-4

1. Mathematics—Study and
teaching (Elementary)
I. Small, Marian
II. Title: Nelson mathematics seven.

QA107.2.N44 2004 Suppl. 1
510   C2004-903421-9

10 | 3-D Geometry

Contents

For helpful information about the chapter, visit **www.mathK8.nelson.com** and follow the links to *Nelson Mathematics 7*, Chapter 10.

The Blackline Masters and answers on pages 76–77 supplement coverage of *The Ontario Curriculum, Grades 1–8: Mathematics, 2005.*

Answers and Solutions

Answers are provided for all questions in the *Student Book*, either in the *Solutions Manual*, in the *Teacher's Resource*, or in the *Student Book* itself. When more than one answer is possible, a sample response is given.

The following questions are answered in the *Student Book*:
- All *Do You Remember?* questions in the *Getting Started* section
- All *Checking* and *Extending* questions in each lesson
- Some *Practising* questions (all those in each lesson that involve two or more calculation steps)
- All *Mid-Chapter Review* and *Chapter Review* questions
- All *Chapter Self-Test* questions
- All *Cumulative Review* multiple-choice questions
- All *Math in Action* questions

The *Student Book* gives only the final answers to these questions, not the explanations or solutions for them.

The following questions are answered in the *Teacher's Resource*:
- All questions in the *Getting Started* activity
- All *Do You Remember?* questions in the *Getting Started* section

- All *Explore the Math* and *Learn About the Math* questions in lessons
- All *Reflecting* and *Checking* questions in each lesson
- The *Key Assessment of Learning Question* in each lesson
- All questions in the *Mental Math*, *Mental Imagery*, and *Curious Math* features
- All *Chapter Self-Test* questions
- All *Chapter Test Master* questions
- All *Chapter Task* questions
- All *Cumulative Review* questions
- All *Chapter Project* questions

The *Teacher's Resource* contains explanations and solutions for these questions.

Complete solutions to the following are in the *Solutions Manual*:
- All *Do You Remember?* questions in the *Getting Started* section
- All *Checking*, *Practising*, and *Extending* questions in each lesson
- All *Mid-Chapter Review* and *Chapter Review* questions
- All *Chapter Self-Test* questions

Chapter 10 Overview

Math Background

The study of geometry and spatial sense provides students with a window to the world around them.

In previous chapters, students have worked with 2-D shapes. They have identified congruent and similar figures and have explored the transformations of geometric figures. In this chapter, students will further their understanding of 3-D geometry and develop their spatial sense by build 3-D shapes from nets and by identifying and sketching a variety of 2-D representations of 3-D objects, including views and isometric drawings. Students will draw models of cube structures, polyhedrons, and 3-D shapes found in the world around them, working from concrete models, diagrams, and photographs.

The use of manipulatives is crucial in helping students to develop their understanding of the characteristics of 3-D shapes. Models of 3-D shapes provide a tool that will help students to visualize a 3-D shape on a 2-D plane and vice versa. Manipulating models and recognizing and sketching different views of 3-D objects from models will help students not only to develop their spatial sense but also extend and apply their understanding of 3-D shapes to the world around them.

Curriculum Across Grades 6 to 8: 3-D Geometry

The Grade 7 expectations listed below are covered in this chapter.
When the expectation is a focus of a particular lesson, the lesson number is indicated in brackets.
When part of the expectation is in square brackets [ ], that part of the expectation is not addressed in the chapter.

Grade 6	Grade 7	Grade 8
Overall Expectations: • sketch three-dimensional figures, and construct three-dimensional figures from drawings	**Overall Expectations:** • develop an understanding of [similarity, and distinguish similarity and congruence] **(1)** • report on [research into real-life] applications of [area] measurements **(7)**	**Overall Expectations:** • develop geometric relationships involving lines, triangles, and polyhedra, and solve problems involving lines and triangles • research, describe, and report on applications of volume and capacity measurement
Specific Expectations: • build three-dimensional models using connecting cubes, given isometric sketches or different views of the structure • determine, through investigation using a variety of tools and strategies, the surface area of rectangular and triangular prisms • sketch, using a variety of tools, isometric perspectives and different views of three-dimensional figures built with interlocking cubes • measure and construct angles up to 180° using a protractor, and classify them as acute, right, obtuse, or straight angles • sketch, suing a variety of tools, isometric perspectives and different views of three-dimensional figures built with interlocking cubes	**Specific Expectations:** • determine, through investigation using a variety of tools, polygons [or combinations of polygons] that tile a plane[, and describe the transformation(s) involved] **(1)** • determine, through investigation using a variety of tools, the surface area of [right] prisms **(1,2)** • sketch different polygonal prisms [that share the same volume] **(3, 4, 5)** • investigate[, using concrete materials,] the angles between the faces of a prism[, and identify right prisms] **(4)** • identify, through investigation, the minimum side and angle information needed [to describe a unique triangle] **(6)**	**Specific Expectations:** • determine, through investigation using concrete materials, the relationship between the numbers of faces, edges, and vertices of a polyhedron • determine, through investigation using concrete materials, the surface area of a cylinder • investigate and describe applications of geometric properties in the real world • determine, through investigation using a variety of tools, relationships among area, perimeter, corresponding side lengths, and corresponding angles of similar shapes

Chapter 10 Planning Chart

Key Concepts

Shapes of different dimensions and their properties can be described mathematically.
There are many representations of 3-D shapes.
Any shape can be created by either combining or dissecting other shapes.
3-D shapes can be located in space. They can be relocated or reoriented using
mathematical procedures.

Chapter Goals

Build three-dimensional (3-D) shapes from nets and with cubes.
Identify 3-D objects that are drawn in different ways.
Recognize different views of 3-D objects.
Sketch different views of 3-D objects from models and drawings.

Student Book Section	Lesson Goal	Pacing 12 days	Prerequisite Skills/Concepts
Getting Started: Colouring Cubes, Do You Remember? pp. 346–347 (TR pp. 11–13)	Use concepts and skills developed prior to this chapter.	1 day	• Identify and classify polygons and polyhedrons. • Identify nets for a variety of polyhedrons from drawings. • Construct polyhedrons from nets. • Design nets of polyhedrons by looking at 3-D models.
Lesson 10.1: Exploration Building and Packing Prisms, pp. 348–349 (TR pp. 14–17)	Build prisms from nets.	1 day	• Classify 2-D shapes according to angle and side properties. • Demonstrate congruence of 2-D and 3-D figures. • Construct prisms from nets. • Determine if a 2-D shape will tessellate a plane. • Apply geometric concepts in real-world situations. • Hypothesize about geometric properties and relationships.
Lesson 10.2: Guided Activity Building Objects from Nets, pp. 350–353 (TR pp. 18–22)	Build 3-D shapes from nets.	1 day	• Identify polyhedrons • Identify nets for a variety of polyhedrons. • Design nets by looking at 3-D models and by using grid and isometric dot paper.
Lesson 10.3: Direct Instruction Top, Front, and Side Views of Cube Structures, pp. 354–357 (TR pp. 23–26)	Recognize and sketch the top, back, front, and side views of cube structures.	1 day	• Visualize the 2-D faces of 3-D objects. • Build a figure with linking cubes and use isometric dot paper to record the design.
Lesson 10.4: Guided Activity Top, Front, and Side Views of 3-D Objects, pp. 360–363 (TR pp. 29–32)	Recognize and sketch the top, front, and side views of 3-D objects.	1 day	• Visualize the 2-D faces of 3-D figures to identify nets for polyhedrons. • Identify and draw views of cube structures.
Lesson 10.5: Direct Instruction Isometric Drawings of Cube Structures, pp. 364–367 (TR pp. 33–36)	Make realistic drawings of cube structures on triangle dot paper.	1 day	• Identify and draw views of cube structures. • Build a figure with linking cubes and record the design using isometric dot paper.
Lesson 10.6: Guided Activity Isometric Drawings of 3-D Objects, pp. 368–371 (TR pp. 37–40)	Make realistic drawings of 3-D objects on triangle dot paper.	1 day	• Create isometric drawings of cube structures. • Recognize the front, top, and side views of 3-D figures.
Lesson 10.7: Guided Activity Communicating about Views, pp. 372–374 (TR pp. 41–44)	Use mathematical language to describe views of 3-D objects.	1 day	• Draw and construct 3-D objects from nets. • Sketch views of 3-D objects. • Use mathematical language to describe geometric ideas.
Mid-Chapter Review: pp. 358–359 (TR pp. 27–28) **Chapter Self-Test:** p. 377 (TR p. 47) **Chapter Review:** pp. 378–379 (TR pp. 48–49)	**Chapter Task:** p. 380 (TR pp. 50–51) **Mental Imagery:** p. 349 (TR p. 17) **Math Game:** p. 375 (TR p. 45) **Curious Math:** p. 376 (TR p. 46) **Chapter Project** (TR pp. 8–9)	4 days	

Materials	Masters	Related Review Questions
coloured pencils scissors tape ruler	2 cm Grid Paper, Masters Booklet, p. 36 *Optional:* Scaffolding for Getting Started Activity, pp. 60–61 *Optional:* Scaffolding for Do You Remember? Questions 1–11, pp. 62–64 *Assessment:* Initial Assessment Summary, Masters Booklet p. 1	
scissors tape protractor *Optional:* 3-D models (triangular, square-based, pentagonal, and hexagonal prisms) and stickers	Nets of Prisms, pp. 53–54 *Assessment:* Problem Solving Rubric, Masters Booklet, p. 8 Workbook, p. 105	Chapter Review Practice Question 1
ruler scissors tape *Optional:* protractor and/or octagon shape for tracing *Optional:* 3-D models	2 cm Grid Paper, Masters Booklet, p. 36 2.5 cm Triangle Dot Paper, Masters Booklet, p. 39 Workbook, pp. 106–107	Mid-Chapter Review Practice Questions 1, 2, 3, 4 Chapter Review Practice Question 2
linking cubes, 22/student ruler	Building Mat, p. 55 1 cm Grid Paper, Masters Booklet, p. 34 *Optional:* Scaffolding for Lesson 10.3, p. 65 Workbook, p. 108	Mid-Chapter Review Practice Questions 5, 6, 7, 8 Chapter Review Practice Question 3
scissors tape coloured pencils ruler *Optional:* 3-D models	Building Mat, p. 55 2 cm Grid Paper, Masters Booklet, p. 36 1 cm Triangle Dot Paper, Masters Booklet, p. 38 Workbook, p. 109	Chapter Review Practice Questions 4, 5, 6
linking cubes ruler coloured pencils	1 cm Triangle Dot Paper, Masters Booklet, p. 38 *Optional:* Scaffolding for Lesson 10.5, Question 7, p.66 Workbook, p. 110	Chapter Review Practice Question 7
ruler 3-D models *Optional:* linking cubes	1 cm Triangle Dot Paper, Masters Booklet, p. 38 Workbook, p. 111	Chapter Review Practice Question 8
scissors tape linking cubes	1 cm Grid Paper, Masters Booklet, p. 34 2 cm Grid Paper, Masters Booklet, p. 36 1 cm Triangle Dot Paper, Masters Booklet, p. 38 Workbook, p. 112	
Mid-Chapter Review: See TR p. 27–28 *Chapter Self-Test:* See TR p. 47 *Chapter Review:* See TR pp. 48–49 *Chapter Task:* See TR pp. 50–51 *Mental Imagery:* See TR p. 17 *Math Game:* See TR p. 45 *Curious Math:* See TR p. 46 *Chapter Project:* See TR pp. 8–9, 70	Mid-Chapter Review—Study Guide, p. 55 Mid-Chapter Review—Frequently Asked Questions, p. 56 Chapter Review—Study Guide, p. 57 Chapter Review—Frequently Asked Questions, p. 58 Chapter Project: Design a Building, p. 70	

Planning for Assessment

Using Nelson Mathematics Assessment Tools

The set of assessment tools in Nelson Mathematics will help students, teachers, administrators, and parents to better understand what it means to produce quality work in mathematics. Rather than just "scoring" student work, these tools describe achievement in mathematics according to the four provincial categories: *Knowledge and Understanding, Application of Learning, Problem Solving/Thinking,* and *Communication.*

- *Assessment Tool 1 (Initial Assessment Summary)* is used in conjunction with the Getting Started lesson that opens each chapter. It is a place to record your observations and concerns about the prior knowledge and skills students bring to a new chapter.
- *Assessment Tool 2 (What to Look for When Assessing Student Achievement)* and *Tool 3 (Coaching Students Toward Success)* clarify for teachers and students respectively what to look for and aim for with respect to each of the four achievement categories.
- *Assessment Tool 4 (Student Interview Form with Prompts)* and *Tool 5 (Student Interview Form without Prompts)* enable you to record anecdotal notes during in-class interviews with your students.
- *Assessment Tools 6 through 9* are the detailed rubrics, or scales, that provide the foundation for assessment in this resource. One scale corresponds to each of the provincial achievement categories: You will use only selected criteria from one of the scales when assessing student learning.
- *Assessment Tools 10* and *11* help teachers to track and organize achievement data from their entire mathematics program for purposes of evaluation and reporting. *The Assessment of Learning Summary—Individual Student* or *Class by Strand* provides teachers with a way to gather data simultaneously by strand and achievement category. The *Individual Student* version *(Tool 10)* permits much greater detail and is especially helpful when speaking to parents about a student's strengths and needs. The *Class by Strand* version *(Tool 11)* may be preferable for very large classes. Each of these tracking charts is accompanied by a sample and set of guidelines for its use.
- As a reporting period approaches, teachers are encouraged to refer to the four generic assessment scales *(Assessment Tools 6–9)* to help determine each student's most consistent level of achievement in each of the categories: *Knowledge and Understanding, Application of Learning, Problem Solving/Thinking,* and *Communication.*
- *Assessment Tool 12* enables you to record and summarize for the report card the learning skills data that have been gathered during a term.

Managing Initial Assessment

- Refer to the specific suggestions for Getting Started in the assessment charts on page 13.
- Use other initial assessments involving informal interviews or Written Answers.
- Use the *Initial Assessment Summary (Tool 1)* to help you record observations/concerns about a student's prior knowledge. You may choose to record observations for all students, or for only those individuals who appear to have difficulty.

Managing Assessment for Feedback

- Refer to the specific suggestions in the Assessment for Feedback charts for Lessons 10.1 to 10.7, found on these pages: 14, 18, 23, 29, 33, 37, and 41.
- Use other informal assessments involving ongoing observations and interviews to help you adapt your instruction to suit individual students' needs.
- Use any of these tools to help you improve student achievement: *What to Look for When Assessing Student Achievement* (Tool 2), *Coaching Students Toward Success* (Tool 3), *Student Interview Form (with prompts)* (Tool 4), *Student Interview Form (without prompts)* (Tool 5).
- **Peer Assessment:** Good opportunities for informal peer assessment occur in all lessons in this chapter and the Math Game: Fishing for Solids (Student Book p. 375).
- **Self-Assessment:** Students can practise and assess what they know by doing the suggested homework.
- **Journal Writing:** Good opportunities for journal writing occur in the Reflecting or the Follow-Up section in any lesson.

Managing Assessment of Learning

- Refer to the chart below, which indicates where to find detailed support for all the Key Assessment of Learning Questions in the lessons, and all the questions in the Mid-Chapter Review and Chapter Review, as well as the Chapter Task. Which of these opportunities you choose to assess will depend on the quantity of evidence you need to gather for individual students. **NOTE:** When charts show levels of student achievement, they are always based on the appropriate parts of the four generic assessment rubrics.
- If you want to assess other questions from the lessons, use the appropriate rows from the four generic rubrics to create your own question-specific rubric.
- To help you track student achievement, use either the *Assessment of Learning Summary—Individual Student (Tool 10)* or *Assessment of Learning Summary—Class by Strand (Tool 11).*
- **Self-Assessment:** After students have completed the chapter, they can try the Chapter Self-Test.
- **Chapter Project:** Interested students can try this as an alternate performance assessment. (Refer to the master on page 70 and the teaching notes on pages 8–9.)

Managing Assessment of Learning Skills

Teachers in Ontario are required to gather data for, and report on, students' demonstration of learning skills in a way that is quite separate from achievement data. The Preparation and Planning box suggests those learning skills that may be assessed during each lesson. You may wish to use the *Assessment of Learning Skills Chart* (Tool 12) to record and manage this data. See page 15 in the *Masters Booklet* for suggestions on using this chart.

Managing Chapter Evaluation

Look at all the assessment data you've recorded throughout the chapter, including information from the Chapter Task, the Chapter Self-Test, or the Chapter Project. Determine the most consistent level for an individual.

Grade 7 ON Chapter 10 Assessment Chart Summary

Student Book Lesson	Assessment for Feedback Chart	Assessment of Learning and Summative Assessment		
		Chart	Key Assessment Question/Category	Strategy
Lesson 10.1: Exploration Building and Packing Prisms, pp. 348–349	TR p. 14	TR p. 17	entire exploration, Problem Solving/Thinking	investigation
Lesson 10.2: Guided Activity Building Objects from Nets, pp. 350–353	TR p. 18	TR p. 22	10, Problem Solving/Thinking	written answer, skills demonstration
Lesson 10.3: Direct Instruction Top, Front, and Side Views of Cube Structures, pp. 354–357	TR p. 23	TR p. 26	6, Application of Learning	written answer
Mid-Chapter Review, p. 359 (This chart is posted on the Nelson Web site **www.mathK8.nelson.com**. It does not appear in this *Teacher's Resource*.)			1, Knowledge and Understanding	short answer
			2, Knowledge and Understanding	written answer
			3, Problem Solving/Thinking	written answer
			4, Application of Learning	short answer
			5, Application of Learning	written answer
			6, Application of Learning	written answer
			7, Application of Learning	written answer
			8, Application of Learning	skills demonstration, written answer
Lesson 10.4: Guided Activity Top, Front, and Side Views of 3-D Objects, pp. 360–363	TR p. 29	TR p. 32	12, Application of Learning	written answer
Lesson 10.5: Direct Instruction Isometric Drawings of Cube Structures, pp. 364–367	TR p. 33	TR p. 36	7, Application of Learning	written answer
Lesson 10.6: Guided Activity Isometric Drawings of 3-D Objects, pp. 368–371	TR p. 37	TR p. 40	5, Application of Learning	written answer
Lesson 7: Guided Activity Communicating About Views, pp. 372–374	TR p. 41	TR p. 44	6, Communication	written answer
Chapter Review, p. 379 (This chart is posted on the Nelson Web site **www.mathK8.nelson.com**. It does not appear in this *Teacher's Resource*.)			1, Problem Solving/Thinking	written answer
			2, Knowledge and Understanding	short answer
			3, Application of Learning	short answer, skills demonstration
			4, Application of Learning	written answer
			5, Knowledge and Understanding	short answer
			6, Application of Learning	short answer, skills demonstration
			7, Application of Learning	written answer
			8, Application of Learning	written answer
Chapter Task: Gift Box Contest, p. 380		TR p. 51	entire task, Problem Solving/Thinking	performance assessment

Teaching Notes for Chapter Project: Design a Building

Related Expectations

Geometry

- determine, through investigation using a variety of tools, the surface area of right prisms

Preparation and Planning

Pacing	Duration of the unit
Materials	• ruler • scissors • tape • *Optional:* 3-D models • Chapter Project: Design a Building (Master) p. 70 • Building Mat (Master) p. 54 • *Optional:* Nets of Prisms (Master) pp. 52–53 • 1 cm Grid Paper, Masters Booklet p. 34 • 2 cm Grid Paper, Masters Booklet p. 36 • 1 cm Triangle Dot Paper, Masters Booklet p. 38 • 2.5 cm Triangle Dot Paper, Masters Booklet p. 39
Enabling Activities	• Building and packing prisms (See Lesson 10.1) • Building objects from nets (See Lesson 10.2) • Top, front, and side views of 3-D objects (See Lesson 10.4) • Isometric drawings of 3-D objects (See Lesson 10.6)
Nelson Web Site	Visit **www.mathK8.nelson.com** and follow the links to *Nelson Mathematics 7*, Chapter 10.

Introducing the Chapter Project

Provide interested students with copies of **Chapter Project: Design a Building p. 70**, and provide examples of interesting and famous buildings that you might find on the Internet or in books, such as Falling Water, designed by the architect Frank Lloyd Wright and located in Pennsylvania, or the Taj Mahal in Agra, India, which was built as a mausoleum for the mughal Empress Mumtaz Mahal.

Ask questions such as:
- What polygons and polyhedrons can you identify in the buildings you have been shown?
- Are some polyhedrons better than others for designing buildings? Explain.
- What are some various functions a building may have? (home, school, store, office, factory, hospital, movie theatre, radio station, movie studio, …)
- Why is it important for an architect to consider the function of a building when creating a design?
- What other factors might an architect need to consider? (location, weather, budget, taste of client, …)

Completing the Chapter Project

Answers to the Questions

A. For example, my building will be a museum of fashion. It should be elegant and eye-catching, like designer clothes, with different floors for displaying clothes from different periods. There needs to be a part for the displays, and a part for the museum offices.

B. For example, I used three copies of a rectangular prism and one hexagonal prism. The rectangular prisms will be the space used for displays of clothes, and the offices for museum staff will be in the hexagonal prism.

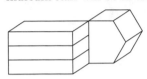

C. For example,

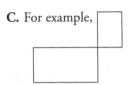

D. For example,

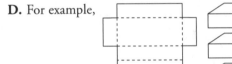

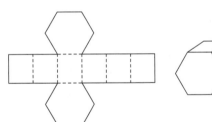

E. For example,

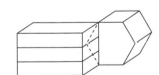

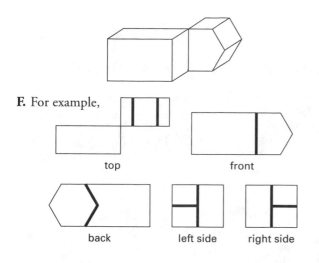

F. For example,

top

front

back

left side

right side

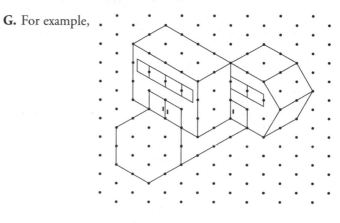

G. For example,

Assessing Students' Work

- Use the Chapter Project Rubric below to assess student work.

Assessment of Learning—What to Look for in Student Work...			
LEVEL 1	**LEVEL 2**	**LEVEL 3**	**LEVEL 4**
Knowledge and Understanding			
Depth of Understanding	• demonstrates a **limited** or **inaccurate** understanding of concept(s)	• demonstrates **some** understanding of concept(s)	• demonstrates **considerable** understanding of concept(s)	• demonstrates **thorough** understanding of concept(s)
Problem Solving/Thinking			
Do: Carry Out the Plan	• use of procedures includes **major errors and/or omissions**	• use of procedures includes **several errors and/or omissions**	• use of precedures is mostly correct, but there may be a **few minor errors and/or omissions**	• use of procedures includes **almost no errors or omissions**
Application of Learning			
Making connections within and between various context	• demonstrates **limited** to make connections between mathematics and the real world	• demonstrates **some** ability to make connections between mathematics learning and the real world	• demonstrates **considerable** ability to make connections between mathematics learning and the real world	• demonstrates **sophisticated** ability to make connections between mathematics learning and the real world
Communication			
Explanation and justification of mathematical concepts, procedures, and problem solving	• provides **limited or inaccurate** explanations/justifications that **lack clarity** or **logical thought** using **minimal** words, pictures symbols and/or numbers	• provides **partial** explanations/justifications that exhibit **some clarity** and **logical thought**, using **simple** words, pictures, symbols, and/or numbers	• provides **complete, clear** and **logical** explanations/justifications, using **appropriate** words, pictures, symbols, and/or numbers	• provides **thorough, clear** and **insightful** explanations/justifications, using a **range** of words, pictures, symbols, and/or numbers
Use of mathematical vocabulary	• uses **very little** mathematical vocabulary, and vocabulary used **lacks clarity and precision**	• uses **some** mathematical vocabulary with **some degree of clarity and precision**	• uses mathematical vocabulary with **considerable clarity and precision**	• uses a **broad range** of mathematical vocabulary to communicate **clearly** and **precisely**

Using the Chapter Opener

Introduce the chapter by discussing the photograph on page 345 of the Student Book. The photograph shows children skateboarding in a skateboard park containing various rails and ramps on which the boarders practice their stunts. Have students find examples of polyhedrons in the photograph, name the polygon shapes of the faces, and look for a polyhedron that is formed from a combination of other polyhedrons.

Also discuss the four goals of the chapter. Ask students to name various polyhedrons they see in the classroom or would see at home or in the community. List the names on the board. Again, have students name the shapes of the 2-D faces of the 3-D shapes. Review the definitions of *prism* and *pyramid* to ensure students understand the differences between these two types of polyhedrons. Have students consider how 3-D shapes may appear differently from different views—top, front and back, and sides.

After discussing the goals, ask students to explain, using examples, why it is important to be able to represent 3-D objects using 2-D drawings.

Using polyhedrons to design a building and a variety of drawings to represent it are the focus of the Chapter Project, which some students may be interested in doing. (Refer to **Chapter Project p. 70** and the teaching notes on pages 8–9.) Links to specific Chapter Project questions are listed at the close of selected lessons, as applicable.

Ask students to record their thoughts about one of the goals in their journals, using a prompt such as, "Some ways to show a 3-D object using a 2-D drawing are …"

At the end of the chapter, ask students to complete the same prompt. Then they can compare their ideas and reflect on what they have learned.

At this time, it would be appropriate to send home **Family Newsletter p. 51**. To focus on important vocabulary, have students look through the chapter and add math word cards to your classroom word wall. Here are some of the terms that are used in the chapter:

• net	• hexagon
• polyhedron	• octagon
• prism	• tetrahedron
• pyramid	• isometric drawing
• pentagon	

CHAPTER 10

3-D Geometry

▶ **GOALS**

You will be able to
- build three-dimensional (3-D) shapes from nets and with cubes
- identify 3-D objects that are drawn in different ways
- recognize different views of 3-D objects
- sketch different views of 3-D objects from models and drawings

Family Newsletter p. 51

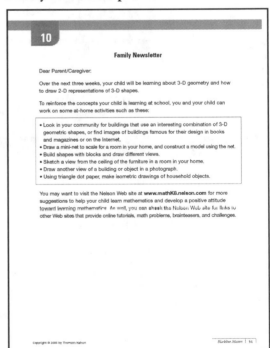

Prerequisite Skills/Concepts

- Sketch three-dimensional figures, and construct three-dimensional figures from drawings

Preparation and Planning

Pacing	**15 min** Activity: Colouring Cubes **30 min** Do You Remember?
Materials	• coloured pencils • scissors • tape • ruler • 2 cm Grid Paper, Masters Booklet p. 36 • *Optional:* Scaffolding for Getting Started Activity (Master) pp. 59–60 • *Optional:* Scaffolding for Do You Remember? (Master) pp. 61–63 • *Assessment:* Initial Assessment Summary, Masters Booklet p. 1
Vocabulary/ Symbols	cube, net, prism, pyramid, face, base, vertices, edges, isosceles, equilateral, quadrilateral, polygon, pentagon, hexagon, octagon, polyhedron, tetrahedron

Activity: Colouring Cubes

(Pairs/Whole Class) ▶ about 15 min

This activity reviews visualizing 3-D shapes from nets and designing a net for a cube.

Start the activity by having students read through the problem. Remind students that a net is a 2-D representation of what a 3-D shape would look like if it were taken apart and laid out flat. Review the definition of *face*—a flat surface (polygon) of a polyhedron—and discuss what is meant by *opposite faces* of a cube.

Provide students with scissors and large grid paper. Have students work with a partner to answer prompts A to E. Bring the class together to share their responses to prompt E. Have students complete prompt F individually. If any students need extra support, guide these students and give them a copy of **Scaffolding for Getting Started Activity pp. 59–60**.

Answers for the Activity

B. a)

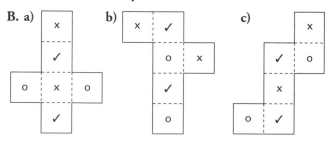

c)

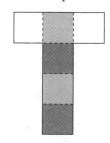

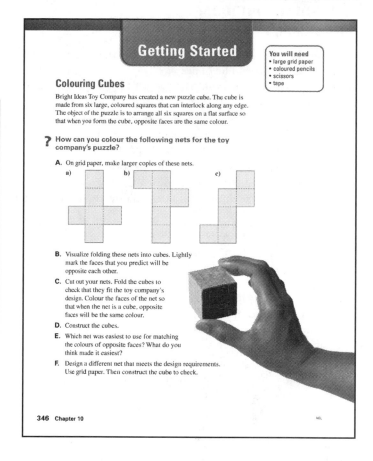

Getting Started

You will need
- large grid paper
- coloured pencils
- scissors
- tape

Colouring Cubes

Bright Ideas Toy Company has created a new puzzle cube. The cube is made from six large, coloured squares that can interlock along any edge. The object of the puzzle is to arrange all six squares on a flat surface so that when you form the cube, opposite faces are the same colour.

? How can you colour the following nets for the toy company's puzzle?

A. On grid paper, make larger copies of these nets.
a)   b)   c)

B. Visualize folding these nets into cubes. Lightly mark the faces that you predict will be opposite each other.

C. Cut out your nets. Fold the cubes to check that they fit the toy company's design. Colour the faces of the net so that when the net is a cube, opposite faces will be the same colour.

D. Construct the cubes.

E. Which net was easiest to use for matching the colours of opposite faces? What do you think made it easiest?

F. Design a different net that meets the design requirements. Use grid paper. Then construct the cube to check.

346 Chapter 10

C. a)   **b)**   **c)**

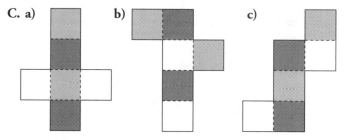

E. For example, the net in part a) was easiest. It was the easiest because each pair of opposite faces had one face in between them on the net.

F. For example,

Do You Remember?
(Individual) ♦ about 30 min

Go over the questions with students before they start to work. Point out the following:

- For Question 1, review the definitions of *isosceles triangle* (2 sides equal in length) and *equilateral triangle* (all sides equal in length). Only rough sketches are needed, so long as students use ticks to indicate equal sides. The pentagon, hexagon, and octagon need not be regular polygons.

- Review the differences and similarities between a *pyramid* and a *prism*, and the relationship between the number of sides of the base and the number of faces in a pyramid and prism.

- For Question 5, review the definition of *tetrahedron* (a 3-D figure with four faces that are polygons).

- Before students begin Question 12, review the definition of *regular polygon* (all sides equal and all angles equal). For this question, students will need a ruler, and some may find grid paper helpful in creating a net. For part a), advise students to avoid drawing complicated polygons or ones with dents, as this will make it difficult, in part b), to create a net for a prism that has the polygon as a base.

- Students should add vocabulary and definitions to their journals for any terms that are new to them or for which they have difficulty recalling the meaning.

Observe individual students to see whether they can answer the questions correctly. If any students need extra support, guide these students and/or give them a copy of **Scaffolding for Do You Remember? pp. 61–63**.

Answers for Do You Remember?

1. **a)** 2 equal sides 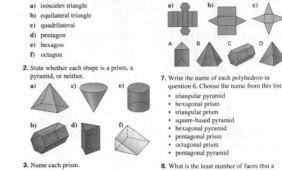 **b)** 3 sides, all sides equal

   c) 4 sides   **d)** 5 sides

   e) 6 sides   **f)** 8 sides

2. **a)** pyramid   **b)** prism   **c)** neither
   d) prism   **e)** neither   **f)** prism

3. **a)** pentagonal prism   **b)** octagonal prism
   c) rectangular prism

4. **a)** hexagonal pyramid   **b)** triangular pyramid
   c) pentagonal pyramid

5. The pyramid in part b) is a tetrahedron.

6. **a)** C   **b)** A   **c)** D

7. **A:** triangular prism
   B: pentagonal pyramid
   C: hexagonal prism
   D: square-based pyramid

8. 4 faces

9. 6 edges

10. 4 vertices

11. A polygon is a 2-D closed shape whose sides are straight lines. A polyhedron is a 3-D figure with faces that are polygons.

12. **a)** For example,

    b) For example,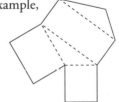

    c) For example,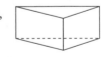

    The vertical faces of this prism are not congruent, because the sides of the polygon base are not equal in length.

Initial Assessment	What You Will See Students Doing...	
Colouring Cubes	**When students have an area of strength**	**If students have an area of need**
• Prompt B (Knowledge and Understanding)	• Students will use visualization to identify opposite faces on the nets correctly.	• Students may need a manipulative, a cube, in order to help them identify the faces on the nets that will be opposite to one another once the cube is formed.
• Prompt E (Communication)	• Students will explain which net was easiest to use for matching the colours of opposite faces and give a logical reason for their choice.	• Students may not be able to identify why matching the colours of opposite faces is easier on the T-shaped net than the others. Prompt by asking students how many faces will separate two faces of the same colour.

Do You Remember?	**When students have an area of strength**	**If students have an area of need**
• Questions 1, 2, 3, 4, 5, 6, 7, 8, 9, 10, 12 a), b) (Knowledge and Understanding)	• Students will sketch and identify each polygon and polyhedron and match each net to a polyhedron correctly. Students will identify the least number of faces, edges, and vertices a polyhedron can have. They will draw an irregular polygon and a net for a prism with an irregular polygon base, and build the prism from the net.	• If students do not recall the meaning of any of the terms used, or the appearance of specific polygons, provide definitions and examples and have students copy them into their journal. Students may not recall how to match nets to pyramids and prisms. Direct their attention to the shape of the base(s). Some students may need to use 3-D models, including a tetrahedron and a triangular prism, to determine the least number of faces, edges, and vertices a polyhedron can have. Students may draw an irregular polygon that is too difficult to create a net for. Advise them to use a shape with three or four sides and no dents and to draw the rectangles for the side faces running outward off each side, to reduce the amount of measuring needed, not forgetting to add another base at the end of one of the faces.
• Questions 11, 12 c) (Communication)	• Students will explain the difference between a polygon and a polyhedron and the congruency of the vertical faces of the prism in 12, using appropriate math language.	• Students may not be able to explain the difference between a polygon and a polyhedron. Provide manipulatives—pattern blocks and 3-D models—of polygons and polyhedra. Students may see that the vertical faces of an irregular polygon prism are not all congruent, but not be able to explain why this is so. Have them measure the sides of the polygon and compare them to the dimensions of the vertical faces, recording their findings.

Building and Packing Prisms

▶ **Goal**

Build prisms from nets.

Prerequisite Skills/Concepts

- Classify 2-D shapes according to angle and side properties.
- Demonstrate congruence of 2-D shapes and 3-D figures.
- Construct prisms from nets.
- Determine if a 2-D shape will tessellate a plane.
- Apply geometric concepts in real-world situations.
- Hypothesize about geometric properties and relationships.

Expectations

- develop an understanding of [similarity, and distinguish similarity and] congruence
- determine, through investigation using a variety of tools, polygons [or combinations of polygons] that tile a plane[, and describe the transformation(s) involved]
- determine, through investigation using a variety of tools, the surface area of [right] prisms

Assessment for Feedback	What You Will See Students Doing...	
Students will	**When students understand**	**If students misunderstand**
• build prisms from nets	• Students will construct prisms from nets that are provided.	• Some students may have trouble constructing prisms from nets. Have students use 3-D models (triangular, square-based, pentagonal, and hexagonal prisms) as references and tools when constructing nets.
• connect packing prisms whose bases are regular polygons so that there are gaps between them to tessellating a plane	• Students will recognize that the angles inside each polygon base must be a multiple of 360°, and that only three regular polygons (triangle, square, hexagon) fit this criterion.	• Students may not recognize that only the bases of prisms need to be considered (i.e., that the problem reduces to one in 2-D transformational geometry), or they may not recall the conditions for a regular polygon to tessellate. Have students review their work from Lesson 7.8.

Preparation and Planning

Pacing (allow 5 min for previous homework)	**5 min** Introduction **30 min** Teaching and Learning **5 min** Consolidation
Materials	• scissors • tape • protractor • *Optional:* 3-D models (triangular, square-based, pentagonal, and hexagonal prism) and stickers • Nets of Prisms (Master) pp. 52–53 • *Assessment:* Problem Solving Rubric, Masters Booklet, p. 8
Vocabulary/ Symbols	prism, face, base, vertex, angle, tiling a plane
Workbook	p. 105
Learning Skills	Cooperation, Problem Solving
Mathematical Processes	Problem Solving, Reflecting
Key Assessment of Learning Question	Entire exploration* (Problem Solving/Thinking)

* Entire exploration is for Assessment of Learning (See chart on p. 16.)

Meeting Individual Needs

Extra Challenge

- Students can design and assemble nets for prisms with bases that are irregular polygons with three, four, five, or six sides and then follow prompts B to E. They can discover that all triangular prisms pack without gaps, and that some but not all prisms with irregular polygon bases having four, five, and six sides will pack without gaps.

Extra Support

- Provide extra practice in creating and assembling nets of 3-D shapes. Students can trace one face of a 3-D model, then roll the model over an edge without lifting it from the paper, and then trace the next face, placing a sticker on each face after it has been traced.

Math Background

In Chapter 7, students worked with tilings and created tessellations. They learned that the angles at any common vertex in a tessellation add up to 360°, and that some, but not all, regular and irregular polygons can be used to create a tessellation. They now apply this knowledge to a 3-D problem: packing prisms with polygon bases. Many irregular polygons, but only regular polygons with interior angles that are a factor of 360° (those with three, four, or six sides) will tile a plane. Regular polygons with more than six sides have interior angles > 120° and < 180°, which are not factors of 360°.

1. Introduction

(Whole Class) ▶ about 5 min

Tell students that today they will be working with congruent
prisms whose bases are polygons and whose sides are rectangles.
Refer to the previous lesson to recall the difference between a
prism and pyramid and review the concept of congruent 3-D
shapes, referring to the photograph on Student Book p. 348.

Sample Discourse

"What is the difference between a prism and a pyramid?"

• *A prism has opposite polygon bases that are congruent and
faces that are parallelograms. A pyramid has a polygon as
its base and triangular faces that meet at a vertex.*

"What must match if two polygons are congruent?"

• *The corresponding sides must be equal in length, and the
corresponding angles must be equal in size.*

"What must match if two prisms are congruent?"

• *The bases and the corresponding faces of each prism must
be congruent.*

"Today we are going to look at how congruent prisms
are used by companies to package products."

2. Teaching and Learning

(Whole Class/Small Groups) ▶ about 30 min

Explore the Math

With students, read the central question on Student Book page
348. Advise students of the following: they will be packing the
prisms by standing them on their bases and then fitting them
together; they need only make one layer, as in the illustration;
they can rotate the prisms on their bases to get them to fit
together; and the gaps students need to consider are any interior
gaps at a vertex and not spaces left between the outer edges of
the packages and the sides of the shipping carton. Before having
students begin the activity, ask them to consider which of the
geometric concepts they have learned might be applicable to
this problem. Have students working in small groups come up
with a hypothesis. Provide each group with scissors, tape, and
a protractor. Students can create and copy their own nets for
irregular polygons; provide those wishing to experiment with
regular polygons with copies of **Nets of Prisms pp. 52–53**.
Have students work through prompts A to E in groups.

10.1 Building and Packing Prisms

You will need
• nets of prisms
• scissors
• tape
• a protractor

▶ **GOAL**
Build prisms from nets.

Explore the Math

Imagine that your job is to design
efficient packaging. Stores and
shipping companies want
packages that pack into
rectangular shipping cartons
so that there is no wasted
space between packages.
They also want
packages that are
interesting shapes to
attract buyers.

? How can you design packages that will pack into
cartons with no gaps between them?

A. Make several congruent prisms from nets. Use nets whose bases
have three, four, five, or six sides.

B. Do the prisms pack so that there are no gaps?

C. Measure the angles at each vertex where the prisms meet or almost
meet. Add the angle measures.

D. Repeat steps A to C for different congruent prisms until you have
used prisms with three, four, five, and six sides.

E. Summarize your findings about the types of prisms that pack
without gaps.

Reflecting

1. How is packing prisms similar to tiling a plane? How is it different?

2. a) What did you notice about the touching vertices of the prisms
that packed with no gaps?

b) What did you notice when you added the angle measures?
Why did this happen?

348 Chapter 10   **Entire exploration is for Assessment of Learning** NEL
(See chart on page 16.)

**Key Assessment: Entire Exploration
(Problem Solving/Thinking)**

Answers to Explore the Math

B. & C. For example,

Prism Base	Do the prisms pack with no gaps?	Number of angles at vertex where prisms meet	Size of angles	Sum of angles at vertex where prisms meet
3 sides	yes	6	all 60°	6 × 60° = 360°

D. For example,

Prism Base	Do the prisms pack with no gaps?	Number of angles at vertex where prisms meet	Size of angles	Sum of angles at vertex where prisms meet
4 sides	yes	4	90°, 30°, 30°, 210°	90° + 30° + 30° + 210° = 360°
5 sides	yes	3 or 4	145°, 145°, 90° 90°	145° + 145° + 90° = 360° 3 × 90° = 360°
6 sides	yes	3	100°, 130°, 130°	100° + 130° + 130° = 360°

E. The prisms whose angles at the vertex where the prisms
meet add up to 360° pack without gaps.

Reflecting

Students will recall that tiling a plane means covering a plane with shapes without overlapping or leaving gaps. By considering the polygonal bases of prisms and looking at the sum of the interior angle measures of the touching vertices, students will see that packing congruent prisms is similar to tiling a plane. Those working with regular polygon bases will find that, since the interior angles of a regular pentagon are all equal, for the base of the prism to tile, the interior angles of the base must be a factor of 360°.

Answers to Reflecting

1. For example, packing prisms is like tiling a plane because, if the shape of the base tessellates, then the prisms will pack without gaps. The difference is that a plane is 2-D and prisms are 3-D objects, so the prisms must all be the same height as well.

2. a) For example, when the polygons are regular, the angles of the touching vertices are all equal, and there is only one way that the prisms will fit together without gaps. For some polygons that are not regular, the vertices have to be fitted together in two different ways to tile.

b) For the prisms that packed without gaps, the angle measures at each vertex where the prisms met added up to 360°. This is because there are 360° in a circle.

3. a) For example, the number of faces of a shape does not determine whether you can pack with gaps. Any pentagonal prism will have seven faces. But a pentagon that is shaped like a triangle on top of a square will tile a plane, and a regular pentagon will not.

b) For example, the shape of the base of a package must tessellate if you want to pack with no gaps. For packages going into a rectangular carton, prisms with rectangular side faces will give the most efficient use of space, as there will be less or no waste space around edges of the carton.

c) For example, the side faces must all be the same length.

d) For example, the number of vertices of a shape does not determine whether you can pack with gaps. There are prisms whose bases have three, four, five, and six sides that will pack with no gaps, and each of these prisms has a different number of vertices.

e) For example, the interior angles of the base shape need to combine in ways that add up to 360°. If the base of the prism is a regular polygon, the interior angles of the polygon are all equal, so the size of the angles must be a factor of 360°.

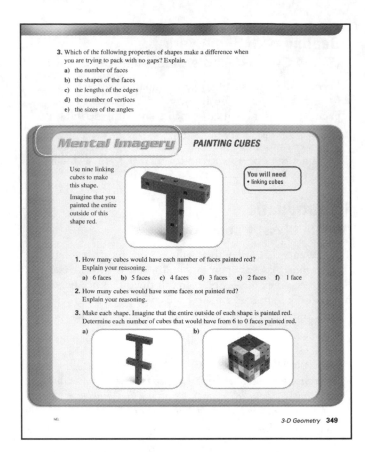

3. Consolidation ◆ about 5 min

Closing (Whole Class)

In their journals, have students summarize their findings about the properties of prisms that pack without gaps and how tessellations can be used to pack objects that are prisms.

Chapter Project Link

In this lesson, students learn about packing prisms so there are no gaps. They can apply and extend their understanding of this concepts in the Chapter Project. (Refer to **Chapter Project: Design a Building p. 71** and the teaching notes on pages 8–9.)

Follow-Up and Preparation for Next Class

- At the end of the class, ask students to select a room in their home and sketch a net for the 3-D shape enclosed by the room's floor, walls (ignore windows and doors), and ceiling.

Assessment of Learning—What to Look for in Student Work...

Assessment Strategy: investigation
Problem Solving/Thinking

Assessment Opportunity
In this exploration lesson, the entire investigation is an opportunity for assessment. You will see students making several congruent prisms from nets. The prisms will have three, four, five, and six sides. Students will draw conclusions about the conditions necessary for prisms to pack with no gaps.

To gather evidence about a student's ability to problem solve, use informal observation, questioning, and written work. Use the Problem Solving/Thinking Rubric (Tool 6) to help you focus on the problem-solving process. You may want to focus on the "Carry Out the Plan", "Review Solution", and "Communicate" rows in the rubric.

Mental Imagery: Painting Cubes

Using Mental Imagery

Materials: linking cubes, 10/student

Distribute linking cubes to each student, nine of one colour and one of another. Begin with the cube that is a different colour. Have students follow you as you attach cubes to each face of this cube, one face at a time. Ask how many faces of the original cube are still showing in each case. Ask students if they notice a relationship between the number of cubes attached and how many faces of the original cube remain uncovered (6 faces – number of cubes attached = number of faces uncovered).

Read with the students the information on Student Book page 349.

Have students work with a partner to solve each question orally. If needed, students could build the shapes with linking cubes.

Answers to Mental Imagery

1. **a)** Zero cubes; six faces is every face on a single cube, but each cube in the T shape has at least one face hidden where it attached to another cube.

   b) Three cubes; the end cubes on the T would have five faces each, because they are only attached at one face.

   c) Five cubes; a cube with four faces painted would be attached to another cube at two faces. Three cubes in the stem and one in each arm of the T are like this.

   d) One cube; a cube with three faces painted would be attached to another cube at three faces. The cube that joins the stem and arms of the T is like this.

   e) Zero cubes; a cube with two faces painted would be attached to another cube at four faces.

   f) Zero cubes; a cube with one face painted would be attached to another cube at five faces. The shape would need at least two layers of cubes for this to happen.

2. All the cubes would have some faces that are not painted red. The faces that are attached to another cube would not be painted red, and all the cubes are connected to at least one other cube.

3. **a)**

Faces	6	5	4	3	2	1	0
Cubes	0	5	10	1	1	0	0

   b)

Faces	6	5	4	3	2	1	0
Cubes	0	0	0	8	24	24	8

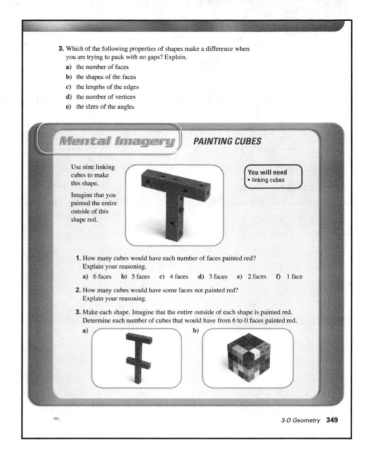

3. Which of the following properties of shapes make a difference when you are trying to pack with no gaps? Explain.
   a) the number of faces
   b) the shapes of the faces
   c) the lengths of the edges
   d) the number of vertices
   e) the sizes of the angles

Mental Imagery — PAINTING CUBES

Use nine linking cubes to make this shape.

Imagine that you painted the entire outside of this shape red.

You will need
• linking cubes

1. How many cubes would have each number of faces painted red? Explain your reasoning.
   a) 6 faces b) 5 faces c) 4 faces d) 3 faces e) 2 faces f) 1 face

2. How many cubes would have some faces not painted red? Explain your reasoning.

3. Make each shape. Imagine that the entire outside of each shape is painted red. Determine each number of cubes that would have from 6 to 0 faces painted red.
   a)   b)

NEL   *3-D Geometry* **349**

Building Objects from Nets

▶ **Goal**

Build 3-D shapes from nets.

Prerequisite Skills/Concepts

- Identify polyhedrons
- Identify nets for a variety of polyhedrons.
- Design nets by looking at 3-D models and by using grid and isometric dot paper.

Expectations

- determine, through investigation using a variety of tools, the surface area of [right] prisms

Assessment for Feedback	What You Will See Students Doing...	
Students will	**When students understand**	**If students misunderstand**
• identify and draw nets for prisms and pyramids	• Students will draw accurate nets for prisms and pyramids based on a diagram of a 3-D object composed of the shapes.	• Some students may neglect to measure the sections of the barn, have trouble measuring a perspective drawing, have difficulty drawing a net using measurements that are not whole numbers, or be unable to reproduce the pentagon in the roof of the barn using only a ruler. Provide prompts concerning which dimensions are needed. Suggest rounding dimensions to the nearest whole number. Have students use a protractor to measure the angles or trace around an octagonal shape and cut the octagon in half through opposite vertices to create the pentagon.
• combine nets to build a 3-D object	• Students will combine nets efficiently to create a single net for the composite object and assemble the net.	• Students may not see how to combine two nets. Have them identify and mark the congruent faces on the two nets where the 3-D shapes join. Some may need to assemble both nets and place them together to see this. Then, have them mark the edges that meet. Encourage them to experiment before settling on a layout for the net.

Preparation and Planning

Pacing (No previous homework was assigned.)	**5 min** Introduction **25 min** Teaching and Learning **15 min** Consolidation
Materials	• a ruler • scissors • tape • 2 cm Grid Paper, Masters Booklet p. 36 • 2.5 cm Triangle Dot Paper, Masters Booklet p. 39
Vocabulary/Symbols	octahedron
Workbook	pp. 106–107
Recommended Practice	7, 8 (Knowledge and Understanding), 9, 10* (Problem Solving/Thinking)
Additional Practice	10, 11, 12 (Application of Learning) **Extending:** 13, 14 (Communication)
Learning Skills	Use of information, Initiative
Mathematical Processes	Selecting Tools and Computational Strategies Connecting

*Key Assessment of Learning Question (See chart on p. 22.)

Meeting Individual Needs

Extra Challenge

- Students can create a 3-D shape by combining three simple polyhedrons (for example, three different rectangular prisms) or two more challenging shapes (for example, a triangular and a pentagonal prism). They can draw a net for each shape used to make the object, and then draw a single net for the object.

Extra Support

- Have students draw nets for cubes, rectangular prisms, and three- and four-sided pyramids by tracing the faces of 3-D models. Then, have them combine the nets for two simple-to-connect shapes (for example, two cubes joined, then two rectangles with congruent bases) before tackling combinations that are more challenging to draw and visualize.

Math Background

A net is one way to represent a 3-D shape using a 2-D drawing. Just as 2-D shapes can be joined to make new 2-D shapes, 3-D shapes can be joined to make new 3-D shapes. It follows that two nets can be combined to make a single net for a new shape. The parts of the faces where the 3-D shapes connect will no longer be needed in the net. When two polyhedrons are joined at congruent faces, both of the faces and all their edges will be eliminated.

1. Introduction
(Whole Class) ◗ about 5 min

If students were assigned the Follow-up and Preparation for Next Class in Lesson 10.1, have students display the nets they created of a room in their home and identify the corresponding 3-D shape, or combination of shapes.

Discuss strategies students can use to match nets with 3-D shapes.

Sample Discourse

"What are some strategies you can use to match 3-D shapes and nets?"

• *You can ask yourself how many faces a type of polyhedron has and see if number of faces = number of sections on the net. If not, the net and shape can't match.*

Discuss examples, such as:

Polyhedron	Number of faces	Number of sections on net
pentagonal prism	7	7
pentagonal pyramid	6	6
hexagonal prism	8	8
hexagonal pyramid	7	7

• *Look at the 2-D shapes of the sections of the net and see if they match the faces of the 3-D shape. There must be one congruent face for each section of the net.*

Draw and discuss examples, such as:

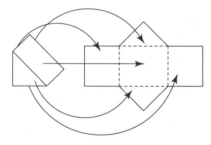

• *Visualize which edges will connect.*

Discuss examples, such as:

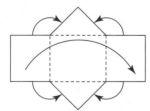

Provide students with 3-D models and have them experiment making new polyhedrons by combining two shapes, for example:

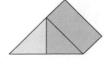

Tell students that today they will be combining nets of polyhedrons to create models of 3-D objects.

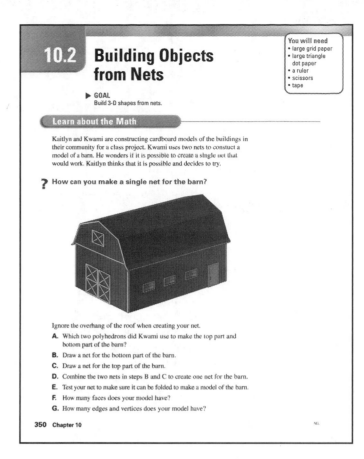

2. Teaching and Learning
(Pairs) ◗ about 25 min

Learn about the Math

With students, read the problem in Learn about the Math on Student Book page 350. Distribute copies of large grid paper to students. Have students work in pairs to complete prompts A to G.

Prompts B–C Have students make full nets for the rectangular prism (the bottom part of the barn) and pentagonal prism (the roof).

Prompt C Students should now remove from each net the side that is hidden when the roof is placed over the bottom of the barn.

Answers to Learn about the Math

A. bottom: rectangular prism, top: pentagonal prism

B. For example,

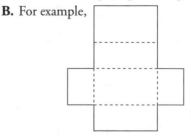

C. For example,

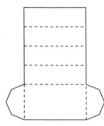

D. For example,

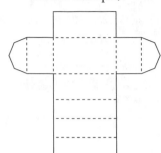

F. 9 faces, including the floor

G. 21 edges, 14 vertices

Reflecting

Here students reflect on the information needed to create a net and the requirements for combining nets. They also consider how changes to a 3-D shape may require changes in the organization of a net for the shape. Look for initiative in creating efficient nets and finding ways to use measurements, proportion, and symmetry to construct 2-D shapes (such as an isosceles triangle or an octagon) that do not lend themselves to being drawn on grid or triangle dot paper.

Answers to Reflecting

1. To build a model, you need the measurement of the width and length of the barn, the height of the walls, the width of a section of the roof, and the height of the roof. You can draw the pentagon at the ends of the roof by finding the midpoint of the base, drawing an isosceles triangle the height of the roof, finding the midpoints of the short sides of that triangle, and then drawing lines the length of a section of the roof that connect the base of the roof and the top point of the roof. Or, you can measure the inside angles of the pentagon using a protractor.

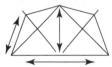

2. For example, the part of the net that represents the roof would have to be joined to a different edge to allow you to add the overhang.

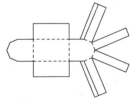

3. If there is a common edge to both nets then they can be joined.

4. For example, I started by folding all the horizontal folds, working from one side to the other, and then I folded the vertical folds. That way I didn't often have to open out a fold I had already done to be able to fold another fold.

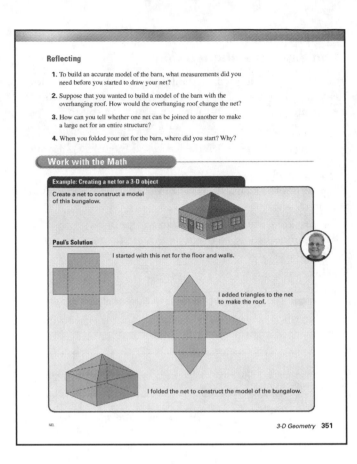

3. Consolidation ♦ about 15 min

Work with the Math

Solved Example (Whole Class)

Discuss with students how the method shown here is the same as that used in Learn About the Math, except that the step of creating separate nets for the component polyhedrons and then combining the nets has been omitted. Note that Paul determined that the bungalow was composed of a rectangular prism and a square-based pyramid before beginning to create the net. He made the rectangular prism first, omitting the top base, and then added the triangular faces of the pyramid, omitting the pyramid's base. Encourage students to use visualization to streamline finding a solution to problems of this kind; at the same time, encourage them to first make full nets for the polyhedron parts if they run into difficulties.

A Checking (Whole Class)

If any students have difficulty visualizing the shapes in Questions 5 and 6, provide models of a cube and square-based pyramid. Students will need large grid paper and large triangle dot paper for creating the net in Question 6.

Answers to Checking

5. a) square-based pyramid, rectangular prism; The square-based pyramid is the roof, resting on the rest of the house, which is the rectangular prism.
   b) 4 edges
   c) 9 faces

6. a) net A; The centre rectangle is the base, the other four rectangles will form the walls, and the triangles form the roof. No matter how you fold net B, some of the triangles will always overlap, so it won't form the model.

B Practising (Individual)

These questions provide practice in matching nets to polyhedrons, including composite polyhedrons, and in creating nets based on 2-D representations.

Students may need their supply of large grid paper and large triangle dot paper replenished. Encourage students to consider carefully whether the net for a given shape can be drawn more efficiently using a ruler and measurements than grid paper or triangle dot paper, and if not, whether grid or dot paper will be most helpful in creating the net.

Some students may be more comfortable using 3-D models, to help identify polyhedrons, and to trace around to draw nets.

10. For part c), including a top for the prism in the net is optional; for part d), however, students should create a net that will form a box in which both the bottom of the lid and the top of the base are open.

Answer to Key Assessment of Learning Question

10. (Problem Solving/Thinking)
   a) bottom: hexagonal prism; lid: hexagonal pyramid
   b) For example,

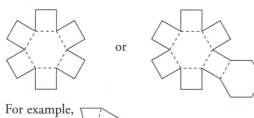

   c) For example,

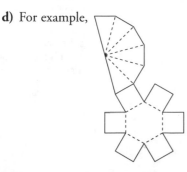

   or

   d) For example,

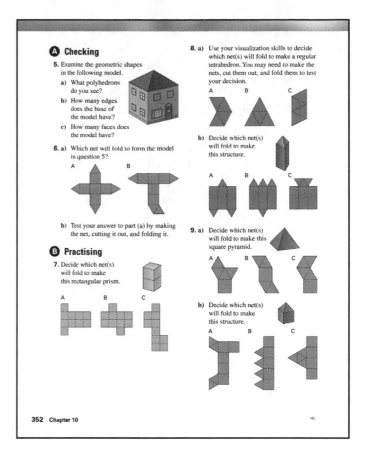

Extending (Pairs/Individual)

These questions provide practice for students in creating nets for unusual shapes, which consist of two or more regular polyhedrons. Students will need large grid paper.

Closing (Whole Class)

Near the end of the class, have students summarize what they have learned by asking the following questions:
- "What two things do you need to know to be able to create a net for a specific prism?"
- "What must two nets have in common if they are to be combined?"
- "If you combine two nets, will the new net have more faces than the original two nets had altogether, the same number, or fewer?"

Chapter Project Link

In this lesson, students learn about building models of 3-D shapes by combining nets of pyramids and prisms. They can apply this skill and extend their understanding of the concepts in the Chapter Project. (Refer to **Chapter Project: Design a Building p. 70** and the teaching notes on pages 8–9.)

Follow-Up and Preparation for Next Class

- At the end of the class, ask students to sketch front, back, and side views of the building in which they live.

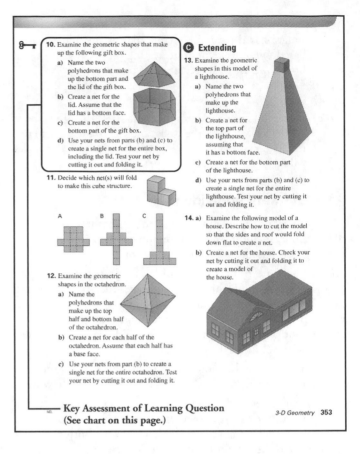

10. Examine the geometric shapes that make up the following gift box.

a) Name the two polyhedrons that make up the bottom part and the lid of the gift box.

b) Create a net for the lid. Assume that the lid has a bottom face.

c) Create a net for the bottom part of the gift box.

d) Use your nets from parts (b) and (c) to create a single net for the entire box, including the lid. Test your net by cutting it out and folding it.

11. Decide which net(s) will fold to make this cube structure.

A   B   C

12. Examine the geometric shapes in the octahedron.

a) Name the polyhedrons that make up the top half and bottom half of the octahedron.

b) Create a net for each half of the octahedron. Assume that each half has a base face.

c) Use your nets from part (b) to create a single net for the entire octahedron. Test your net by cutting it out and folding it.

C **Extending**

13. Examine the geometric shapes in this model of a lighthouse.

a) Name the two polyhedrons that make up the lighthouse.

b) Create a net for the top part of the lighthouse, assuming that it has a bottom face.

c) Create a net for the bottom part of the lighthouse.

d) Use your nets from parts (b) and (c) to create a single net for the entire lighthouse. Test your net by cutting it out and folding it.

14. a) Examine the following model of a house. Describe how to cut the model so that the sides and roof would fold down flat to create a net.

b) Create a net for the house. Check your net by cutting it out and folding it to create a model of the house.

— **Key Assessment of Learning Question** (See chart on this page.)

3-D Geometry **353**

Assessment of Learning—What to Look for in Student Work...

Assessment Strategy: written question, skills demonstration
Problem Solving/Thinking

Key Assessment Question 10

- Examine the geometric shapes that make up the following gift box.
  a) Name the two polyhedrons that make up the bottom part and the lid of the gift box.

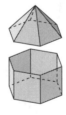

  b) Create a net for the lid. Assume that the lid has a bottom face.
  c) Create a net for the bottom part of the gift box.
  d) Use your nets from parts (b) and (c) to create a single net for the entire box, including the lid. Test your net by cutting it out and folding it.

1	2	3	4
Solve the Problem			
• Uses a strategy and **attempts** to create a net for the octahedron but **does not arrive at an answer**	• Carries out the plan **to some extent**, using a strategy, and develops a **partial and/or incorrect solution**	• Carries out the plan **effectively** by using an **appropriate** strategy and **creating a single net for the octahedron**	• Shows **flexibility** and **insight** when carrying out the plan by **trying** and **adapting**, when necessary, **one or more strategies** to **create a single net for the octahedron**
• Creating a net for the octahedron and testing it includes **major errors and/or omissions**	• Creating a net for the octahedron and testing it includes **several errors and/or omissions**	• Creating a net for the octahedron and testing it is mostly correct, but there may be a **few minor errors and/or omissions**	• Creating a net for the octahedron and testing it includes **almost no errors or omissions**

10.3 Top, Front, and Side Views of Cube Structures

▶ **Goal**

Recognize and sketch the top, back, front, and side views of cube structures.

Prerequisite Skills/Concepts

- Visualize the 2-D faces of 3-D objects.
- Build a figure with linking cubes and use isometric dot paper to record the design.

Expectations

- sketch different polygonal prisms [that share the same volume]

Assessment for Feedback	What You Will See Students Doing...	
Students will	**When students understand**	**If students misunderstand**
• recognize the views of a cube structure	• Students will identify views correctly.	• Students may not look directly at the view, or may allow the structure to move on the mat, and may consequently identify views incorrectly. Prompt them to see that views are 2-D, not 3-D, shapes. Show them how to rotate the mat rather than the structure.
• identify changes of depth on views	• Students will use changes of depth to facilitate connecting views and structures and will draw correct depth lines on views.	• Have students draw views on grid paper and count the number of cubes below/behind each square in the grid. When adjoining squares have a different number, the depth changes between them.
• draw top, front, and side views of a cube structure	• Students will draw correct top, front, and side views of a cube structure given as a concrete example or drawing.	• Students may draw incorrect views. Have students count the cubes in a view row by row, drawing each row on grid paper as it is counted. They can then check their drawing by counting the cubes in the view column by column.

Preparation and Planning

Pacing (allow 5 min for previous homework)	**5 min** Introduction **15 min** Teaching and Learning **20 min** Consolidation
Materials	• linking cubes, 27/student • ruler • Building Mat (Master) p. 55 • 1 cm Grid Paper, Masters Booklet p. 34 • *Optional:* Scaffolding for Lesson 10.3, (Master) p. 65
Vocabulary/ Symbols	footprint (of a building)
Workbook	p. 108
Recommended Practice	6* (Application of Learning), 7 (Knowledge and Understanding), 8
Additional Practice	9 a), b), c) (Problem Solving/ Thinking), 9 c) (Communication), 10, 11 **Extending:** 12, 13, 14
Learning Skills	Cooperation, Class participation
Mathematical Processes	Reasoning and Proving, Reflecting

*Key Assessment of Learning Question (See chart on p. 26.)

Meeting Individual Needs

Extra Challenge

- Students can draw views of objects that are irregular in shape, and then ask a partner to try to identify the 3-D figure from its views.

Extra Support

- Students having difficulty interpreting and representing depth on views can build three versions of a cube structure, with each layer of cubes coloured differently: for the top view, colour layers from top to bottom; for the front and back views, colour layers from front to back; and for the side views, colour layer from side to side. Any change in colour in a view should be marked with a thick dark line.

Math Background

In Lesson 10.2, students considered how polyhedrons can be combined to form new 3-D shapes and used the faces of polyhedrons to create nets. They now consider structures made of unit cubes, and create 2-D representations by combining the vertical faces on a side of the structure, and the horizontal faces on the top, to draw a view. Because a cube's sides are all perpendicular, when a cube structure that sits flat on its base is viewed from the top or a side, the dimensions of the view match the related dimensions of the shape. In comparison, the dimensions of the 2-D shape seen when looking down at a peaked roof, for example, will not match those of the two sides of the roof. Students will identify and draw views for some shapes like this in Lesson 10.4.

1. Introduction
(Whole Class) ▶ about 5 min

If students were assigned the Follow-up and Preparation for Next Class in Lesson 10.2, have students present their sketches of the front, back, and side views of the building in which they live. Ask what parts of the building they found most difficult to draw.

Display some blueprints showing elevations of a building, or reproductions of elevations from books or the Internet. Discuss how architects use drawings like this along with floor plans, and inform students that a scale drawing of the side, front, or back of a building is called an *elevation*.

Sample Discourse

"What do you think architects would use this type of drawing for?"

- *To help clients see what the finished building will look like from different viewpoints. It is hard to visualize that from a floor plan.*

"What can you see in the elevations that you can't see on the floor plans?"

- *How high each floor of the building is, and what the doors and windows will look like.*

"How are the floor plans and the elevations related?"

- *The floor plans are sort of like the bases of prisms, and the elevations like the sides.*
- *The edges of the floor plan are the bottom sides of the views.*

Tell students that today they will be identifying and sketching the top, front, and side views of structures made of cubes.

2. Teaching and Learning
(Whole Class) ▶ about 15 min

Learn about the Math

With students, read the introduction and central question on Student Book page 354. Provide students with linking cubes, grid paper, and copies of **Building Mat p. 54**. Demonstrate how to position a structure on a building mat, so that one side lines up with the edge of the mat. Advise students that

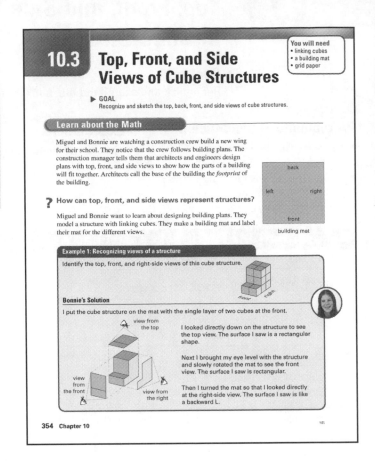

it does not matter, in a cube structure, which side they choose to be the front; the essential thing is to not move the structure once a position has been chosen. Instead, they should either rotate the mat or move themselves to where they can look at each view directly, at eye level.

Tell students they will be using their building mats throughout the remainder of the chapter.

Solved Examples (Pairs/Whole Class)

Have students work through Examples 1 and 2 in pairs, reproducing the structure and drawing the views both freehand (or using a ruler) and on grid paper. Bring the class together to discuss which of the two methods in Example 2 they prefer, and their reasons. Visualizing a view of a 3-D structure as a 2-D shape will come more easily to some students than others. Suggest counting cubes as they look at a view of the structure (How many cubes high? How many cubes wide?) and then the squares outlined on the grid paper to check that a view is correct.

Reflecting

These questions will help students to understand the relationships between the lengths, depths, and heights of a structure and their 2-D representations.

Answers to Reflecting

1. The width of the top view and the width of the front view are equal.

2. The thick dark line on the front view shows that there is a change in depth, but you don't know how much deeper, or which part is deeper, the bottom layer or the top layers. The side view is one cube wider on the bottom, and this shows that the bottom layer is one row of cubes deeper.

3. The height of the front view and the height of the right-side view are equal.

4. Two buildings can have the same front view and different side views if the width and height of the fronts is the same, and there is a change in depth at the same point, but on one building the change in depth is greater than on the other.

3. Consolidation ♦ about 20 min

Work with the Math

Solved Example (Pairs/Whole Class)

Have students work through Example 3 in pairs. Bring students together to discuss how, while depth lines on a view show that there is a change in depth at that point, they do not show how much of a change. To know that, you also need to see other views. For some shapes, you may only need three views to show the shape completely; for others, you will need to see the top, back, front, and both sides.

Ⓐ Checking (Individual/Pairs)

Have students complete the question individually and then compare answers with a partner. Have students make the bottom layer with a different colour of cubes than the top two layers, to reinforce using the depth line to identify views. Remind students to always label each view as soon as they have drawn it.

Answers to Checking

5. **c)** A: left-side; from the left side the L-shape is not visible, the structure looks like three stacked squares, which is shown in A; B: front; from the front, the L-shape is visible, and this is shown in B; C: top; from the top, the structure looks like two squares, which is shown in C.

d)

right

e) left-side view and top view; The dark lines on these views indicate changes in depth.

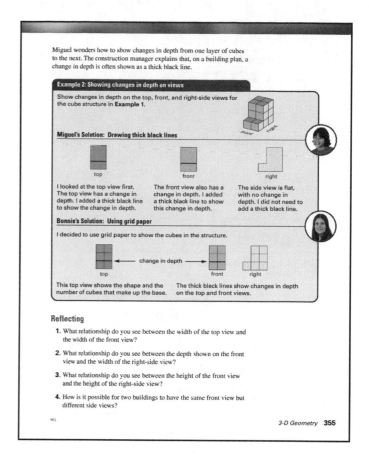

Ⓑ Practising (Individual)

These questions give students opportunities to draw the three views of a given structure, as well as build a structure given the three views. As students will need linking cubes, grid paper, and a building mat for these questions, they will be more easily completed in class than as homework.

6. If students need extra support, guide these students and give them a copy of **Scaffolding for Lesson 10.3, p. 65.**

Answers to Key Assessment of Learning Question

6. (Application of Learning)

b)

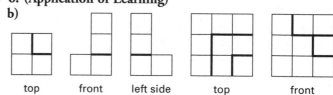

top   front   left side   top   front

Ⓒ Extending (Individual)

Provide linking cubes, grid paper, and building mats. Question 14 requires students to build a structure and draw views of a structure using only written information about the views.

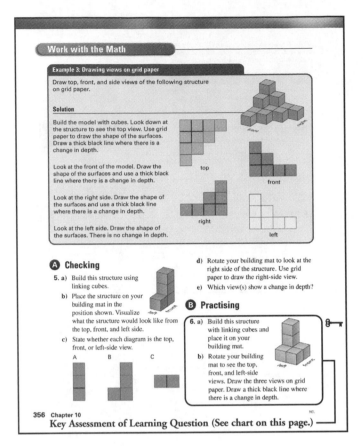

Work with the Math

Example 3: Drawing views on grid paper

Draw top, front, and side views of the following structure on grid paper.

Solution

Build the model with cubes. Look down at the structure to see the top view. Use grid paper to draw the shape of the surfaces. Draw a thick black line where there is a change in depth.

Look at the front of the model. Draw the shape of the surfaces and use a thick black line where there is a change in depth.

Look at the right side. Draw the shape of the surfaces and use a thick black line where there is a change in depth.

Look at the left side. Draw the shape of the surfaces. There is no change in depth.

top

front

right

left

A Checking

5. a) Build this structure using linking cubes.
   b) Place the structure on your building mat in the position shown. Visualize what the structure would look like from the top, front, and left side.
   c) State whether each diagram is the top, front, or left-side view.

   A   B   C

   d) Rotate your building mat to look at the right side of the structure. Use grid paper to draw the right-side view.
   e) Which view(s) show a change in depth?

B Practising

6. a) Build this structure with linking cubes and place it on your building mat.
   b) Rotate your building mat to see the top, front, and left-side views. Draw the three views on grid paper. Draw a thick black line where there is a change in depth.

356 Chapter 10
Key Assessment of Learning Question (See chart on this page.)

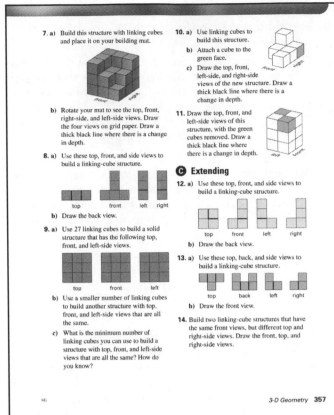

7. a) Build this structure with linking cubes and place it on your building mat.
   b) Rotate your mat to see the top, front, right-side, and left-side views. Draw the four views on grid paper. Draw a thick black line where there is a change in depth.

8. a) Use these top, front, and side views to build a linking-cube structure.

   top   front   left   right

   b) Draw the back view.

9. a) Use 27 linking cubes to build a solid structure that has the following top, front, and left-side views.

   top   front   left

   b) Use a smaller number of linking cubes to build another structure with top, front, and left-side views that are all the same.
   c) What is the minimum number of linking cubes you can use to build a structure with top, front, and left-side views that are all the same? How do you know?

10. a) Use linking cubes to build this structure.
    b) Attach a cube to the green face.
    c) Draw the top, front, left-side, and right-side views of the new structure. Draw a thick black line where there is a change in depth.

11. Draw the top, front, and left-side views of this structure, with the green cubes removed. Draw a thick black line where there is a change in depth.

C Extending

12. a) Use these top, front, and side views to build a linking-cube structure.

    top   front   left   right

    b) Draw the back view.

13. a) Use these top, back, and side views to build a linking-cube structure.

    top   back   left   right

    b) Draw the front view.

14. Build two linking-cube structures that have the same front views, but different top and right-side views. Draw the front, top, and right-side views.

3-D Geometry 357

Closing (Whole Class)

Near the end of the class, have students summarize what they have learned by asking the following question:

- *"What are all the ways you have learned so far to represent a 3-D shape with a 2-D drawing?"*

Follow-Up and Preparation for Next Class

- At the end of the class, ask students to use what they have learned today to improve their sketches of the front, back, and side views of the building in which they live.

Assessment of Learning—What to Look for in Student Work...

Assessment Strategy: written answer
Application of Learning

Key Assessment Question 6
- **a)** Build this structure with linking cubes and place it on your building mat.
- **b)** Rotate your building mat to see the top, front, and left-side views.
  Draw the three views on grid paper.
  Draw a thick black line where there is a change in depth.

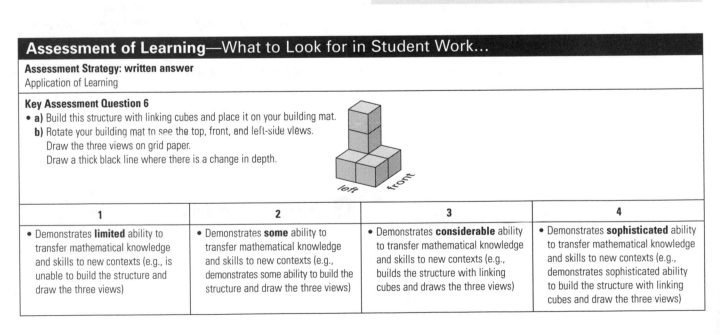

1	2	3	4
• Demonstrates **limited** ability to transfer mathematical knowledge and skills to new contexts (e.g., is unable to build the structure and draw the three views)	• Demonstrates **some** ability to transfer mathematical knowledge and skills to new contexts (e.g., demonstrates some ability to build the structure and draw the three views)	• Demonstrates **considerable** ability to transfer mathematical knowledge and skills to new contexts (e.g., builds the structure with linking cubes and draws the three views)	• Demonstrates **sophisticated** ability to transfer mathematical knowledge and skills to new contexts (e.g., demonstrates sophisticated ability to build the structure with linking cubes and draw the three views)

Preparation and Planning

Materials	• Mid-Chapter Review—Study Guide (p. 56) • Mid-Chapter Review—Frequently Asked Questions (p. 57)

Dealing with Homework
(Whole Class) ▶ about 5 min

Take up Questions 6, 7, and 8 from Lesson 10.3, and work through any questions with which students had difficulty.

Using the Frequently Asked Questions
(Whole Class) ▶ about 10 min

Have students keep their Student Books closed. Write the Frequently Asked Questions on the board, or use **Mid-Chapter Review—Frequently Asked Questions p. 57**. (Distribute the master, or show it on an overhead.) Use the discussion to draw out what the class feels is the best answer to each question. Then have students compare the class answers with the answers on Student Book page 358.

Have students summarize the answers in their own words, as a way of reflecting on the concepts. Students can refer to the answers to the Frequently Asked Questions as they work through the Practice Questions.

Optional: Prepare an overhead transparency of **Mid-Chapter Review—Study Guide p. 56**. Have students share their answers in class. Summarize the answers on a table to which students may refer as they work through the Practice Questions and the remainder of the chapter. Students should copy the completed table into their notes.

Using the Practice Questions
(Individual) ▶ about 10 min

Students should complete all the questions. Most students will probably complete Questions 1 to 5 in class. Assign the rest for homework.

Assessment of Learning

Use the questions on page 359 of the Student Book to assess the following:
• students' knowledge and understanding of concepts developed so far
• students' ability to apply learned procedures
• students' ability to solve problems using the concepts developed in the chapter so far

Refer to the **Knowledge and Understanding Rubric, Masters Booklet p. 9**, to get an overall assessment of students' understanding of the concepts. Visit **www.mathK8.nelson.com** and follow the links to Grade 7, Chapter 10, for assessment of learning charts.

Use **Mid-Chapter Review—Summary, Masters Booklet p. 21**, to record assessment data.

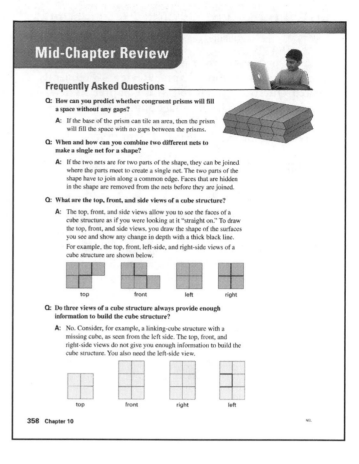

Follow-Up and Preparation for Next Class

- Have students record their answers to the Frequently Asked Questions in their notes. For convenience, provide copies of **Mid-Chapter Review—Frequently Asked Questions p. 56** and **Mid-Chapter Review—Study Guide p. 57**. Encourage students to summarize their understanding of 3-D geometry graphically. If students completed the Follow-Up and Preparation for Next Class activity from Lesson 10.3, they could use linking cubes to create a rough scale model of the building in which they live based on the top, front, and side views they drew. Display students' linking cube models along with the views they drew and post them for comment next class.

Alternatively, weather permitting, students can work in pairs or small groups to produce a small linking-cube model and draw side views of the school building.

Practice Questions

(10.2) **1.** Name the polyhedron that each net represents. You may need to make each net, cut it out, and fold it to find out.

a)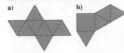
b)

(10.2) **2.** State whether each net will fold to make a box with a lid. If the net will not fold to make a box with a lid, explain why.

a) c)

b) d)

(10.2) **3.** The following dollhouse is under construction and needs walls.

a) Create a net that will fold to make the walls and floor for the dollhouse.

b) Is it possible to create a single net for the entire dollhouse? Explain.

4. Decide which net(s) will fold to make this cube structure. (10.2)

A   B   C

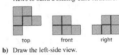

5. a) Build this structure with linking cubes and place it on your building mat.

b) Rotate your mat and draw the top, front, right-side, and left-side views on grid paper. Draw a thick black line where there is a change in depth. (10.3)

6. a) Use linking cubes to build this structure.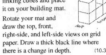

b) Attach a cube to the yellow face.

c) Draw the top, front, left-side, and right-side views of the new structure. Draw a thick black line where there is a change in depth. (10.3)

7. Draw the top, front, and right-side views of this structure, with the yellow cubes removed. Draw a thick black line where there is a change in depth. (10.3)

8. a) Use these top, front, and right-side views to build a linking-cube structure.

top   front   right

b) Draw the left-side view.

c) Draw the back view. (10.3)

3-D Geometry **359**

Top, Front and Side Views of 3-D Objects

▶ **Goal**

Recognize and sketch the top, front, and side views of 3-D objects.

Prerequisite Skills/Concepts

- Visualize the 2-D faces of 3-D figures to identify nets for polyhedrons.
- Identify and draw views of cube structures.

Expectations

- sketch different polygonal prisms [that share the same volume]
- investigate[, using concrete materials,] the angles between the faces of a prism[, and identify right prisms]

Assessment for Feedback	What You Will See Students Doing...	
Students will	**When students understand**	**If students misunderstand**
• identify a polyhedron from diagrams of its views	• Students will identify a polyhedron from diagrams of its views.	• Some students may not be able to visualize a polyhedron from diagrams. Prompt them to look for the view that indicates the shape of the base. Have 3-D models available so that students can compare the views to the faces of the 3-D shapes.
• sketch front, top, and side views of a polyhedron from an illustration of the polyhedron	• Students will be able to sketch the front, top, and side views of a polyhedron from diagrams and photographs of the object.	• Some students may not be able to visualize views of an object shown in an illustration and may need a 3-D model they can physically rotate. Provide 3-D models, but also encourage students to look at the shapes of the views for clues and recall what they know about the shapes of the faces of various types of polyhedrons.

Preparation and Planning

Pacing (allow 5 min for previous homework)	**5 min** Introduction **15 min** Teaching and Learning **20 min** Consolidation
Materials	• scissors • tape • coloured pencils • ruler • Building Mat (Master) p. 55 • 2 cm Grid Paper, Masters Booklet p. 36 • 1 cm Triangle Dot Paper, Masters Booklet p. 38
Vocabulary/ Symbols	pylon
Workbook	p. 109
Recommended Practice	6 (Knowledge and Understanding), 7, 8, 9 a), 10, 11 (Communication), 12* (Application of Learning)
Additional Practice	10 b), 13, 14, 15, 16 (Problem Solving/Thinking) **Extending:** 17, 18, 19 , 20
Learning Skills	Homework Completion, Class Participation
Mathematical Processes	Problem Solving, Representing

*Key Assessment of Learning Question (See chart on p. 32.)

Meeting Individual Needs

Extra Challenge

- Students can sketch views of objects around them (such as those shown in Question 17), and then share their sketches with a partner who can try to identify the object.

Extra Support

- Some students may have difficulty drawing views involving angles and perspective. For drawing equilateral triangles and hexagons, triangle dot paper will be helpful. For other polygons, provide a 3-D model whose base can be traced. Where a view involves perspective, as in the side view of the triangular pyramid in Question 9, have students build a large model of the shape from a net, place the model on a building mat, and then, viewing the object from the side at eye level, hold a ruler horizontally in front of them, lined up with the corner of the pyramid nearest to them. They will see that the base of the side in this 2-D view slants upward, rather than being horizontal.

Math Background

In Lesson 10.5, students worked with concrete cube structures, which can be rotated physically and whose views can easily be represented on grid paper. In this lesson, students work with a variety of diagrams of views and symmetrical 3-D objects. The work done in Lesson 10.2 in breaking polyhedrons into component shapes will be valuable here, as will a familiarity with the definitions of various types of polyhedrons. However, skill at 3-D visualization, and in particular the ability to rotate a 3-D structure visually, varies widely, as does skill in drawing, and a wide variation in students' skills should be expected and accommodated.

Have students compare their answers to Mid-Chapter Review Questions 6, 7, and 8. Discuss any difficulties that may have arisen from these questions.

1. Introduction
(Whole Class) ▶ about 5 min

Recall the work done in Lesson 10.3 with cube structures. Explain to students that in this lesson, they will be asked to identify and sketch the top, front, and side views of polyhedrons and other 3-D objects that are not cube structures and that are only shown in diagrams. Discuss with students what difficulties could be encountered.

Sample Discourse

"What do you think will make recognizing views from drawings rather than a concrete object more challenging?"

• *We could put the cube structure on the building mat and turn the mat. With diagrams, we will need to use visualization.*

"What do you think will make recognizing views of polyhedrons more challenging?"

• *We will need to remember what the faces and bases look like to be able to identify the shape.*

"What makes it easier to draw views of a cube structure?"

• *All the lines are either vertical or horizontal.*
• *All the angles in the structures are 90°.*
• *Each cube is exactly the same size and shape, and each face is a square, so it is easy to reproduce the shapes of the views on grid paper.*

"What do you think will make drawing views of 3-D objects more challenging?"

• *Not all the angles of the 3-D shapes will be right angles, so they will be harder to draw.*
• *The measurements might not all be whole numbers, so it won't be so easy to draw views on a grid.*
• *It might be harder to show depth if there are slanting parts.*

Have students turn to page 360 in the Student Book.

2. Teaching and Learning
(Whole Class/Pairs) ▶ about 15 min

Learn about the Math

Read the introduction and central question with students. Distribute triangle dot paper and large grid paper, rulers, scissors, tape, and coloured pencils. Make sure each student has a copy of **Building Mat p. 54**. Have students work in pairs to complete prompts A to E. Have triangular prisms available for students to use when working on the prompts.

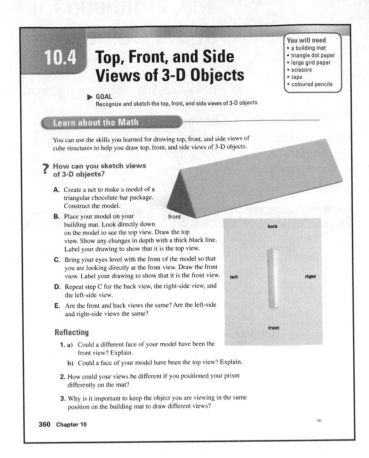

Answers to Learn about the Math

A. For example,

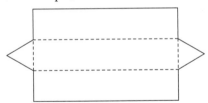

B.

C. △
   front

D. △   □
   back   right side

   □
   left side

E. The front and back views are the same. The left-side and the right-side views are the same.

Reflecting

These questions help students to see that it is vital when drawing views to keep the model in the same position on the building mat.

Answers to Reflecting

1. **a)** yes; The model could be rotated so that a rectangular face is the front view.
   b) no; For a face to be the top view, the model would have to sit on an edge and this is not possible.

2. If you position the prism differently on the mat, then different faces will be in the positions of the different views.

3. If the object on the building mat is moved, one side of the model could accidentally be used for two different views.

3. Consolidation ▶ about 20 min

Work with the Math

Solved Examples (Individual)

Before students read through the solved examples individually, explain that these examples will be looking at polyhedrons and therefore, that the views may not be as obvious as seen in previous examples.

Ⓐ Checking

For Question 4, provide 3-D models for students who may have difficulty identifying the polyhedron. Question 5 is a slight extension of Example 1. Have students refer to the example when working on the question. Views can be drawn on grid paper.

Answers to Checking

4. octagonal prism; It is sitting on its octagonal base.

5.

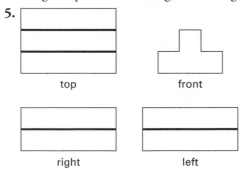

top	front

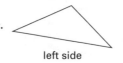

right	left

Ⓑ Practising

These questions provide practice in matching views to and in sketching views of polyhedrons. Have 3-D models available for students to use to help them solve the questions.

9. **b)** The side view of this shape involves perspective.

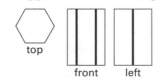

left side

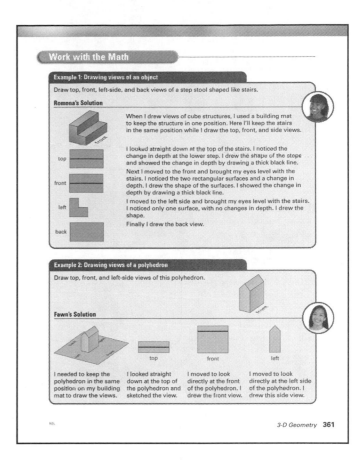

13. Provide students with a 3-D model of an octagon to use to trace for the top view.

14. Provide students with a model of a triangular prism to help them visualize the side view of the tip block.

15. Some students will treat this shape as simply a rectangular prism on top of a cropped square-based pyramid. Others will include depth lines to show the stepped sides and will include the ramp. Either is acceptable.

16. **b)** This question is looking for polyhedrons for which the top, front, and side views are all the same.

17. Students should note that all the objects are symmetrical.

Answer to Key Assessment of Learning Question

⚷—12. (Application of Learning)

top	front	left

Ⓒ Extending

For Questions 17 b) and c), students can sketch an actual computer and cell phone.

For Question 17 a) and d), students can use a toy airplane and truck.

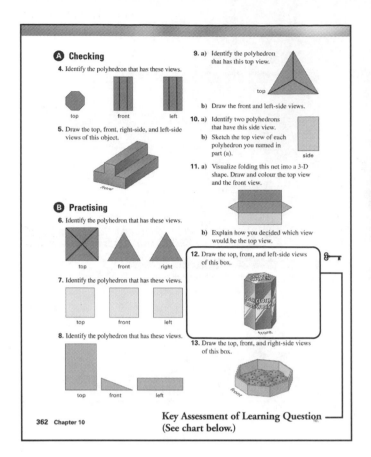

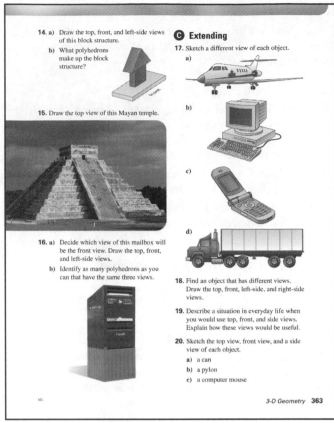

Closing (Whole Class/Pairs)

Near the end of the class, have students summarize what they have learned by asking the following question:
• "What techniques and information can you use to help you draw views of a polyhedron from a diagram?"

Encourage students to use manipulatives to help them with their work.

Chapter Project Link

In this lesson, students learn to recognize and sketch the top, front, and side views of polyhedrons. They can apply and extend their understanding of these skills in the Chapter Project. (Refer to **Chapter Project: Design a Building p. 71** and the teaching notes on pages 8–9.)

Follow-Up and Preparation for Next Class

• In their journals, have students explain the importance of being able to recognize and sketch 3-D objects from different views.

Assessment of Learning—What to Look for in Student Work...

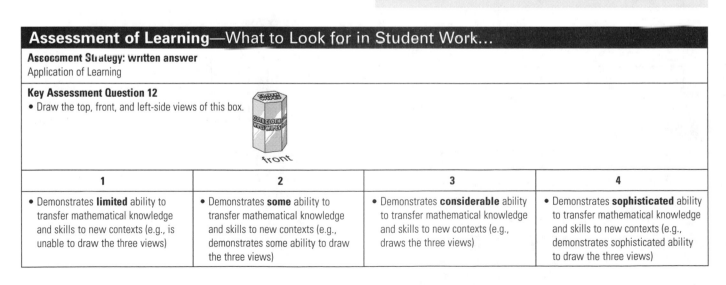

Assessment Strategy: written answer
Application of Learning

Key Assessment Question 12
• Draw the top, front, and left-side views of this box.

1	2	3	4
• Demonstrates **limited** ability to transfer mathematical knowledge and skills to new contexts (e.g., is unable to draw the three views)	• Demonstrates **some** ability to transfer mathematical knowledge and skills to new contexts (e.g., demonstrates some ability to draw the three views)	• Demonstrates **considerable** ability to transfer mathematical knowledge and skills to new contexts (e.g., draws the three views)	• Demonstrates **sophisticated** ability to transfer mathematical knowledge and skills to new contexts (e.g., demonstrates sophisticated ability to draw the three views)

10.5 Isometric Drawings of Cube Structures

▶ **Goal**
Make realistic drawings of cube structures on triangle dot paper.

Prerequisite Skills/Concepts
- Identify and draw views of cube structures.
- Build a figure with linking cubes and record the design using isometric dot paper.

Expectations
- sketch different polygonal prisms [that share the same volume]

Assessment for Feedback	What You Will See Students Doing...	
Students will	**When students understand**	**If students misunderstand**
• make isometric drawings of cube structures on triangle dot paper	• Students will make accurate isometric drawings of cube structures on triangle dot paper from both models and views.	• Some students will have difficulty visualizing a cube structure from a picture. Provide students with linking cubes to construct a concrete example of cube structures. A concrete example will help them to see the layers of the structure and this will facilitate their drawing of the structure.

Preparation and Planning

Pacing (allow 10 minutes for homework)	**5 min** Introduction **15 min** Teaching and Learning **20 min** Consolidation
Materials	• linking cubes • a ruler • coloured paper • 1 cm Triangle Dot Paper, Masters Booklet p. 38 • *Optional:* Scaffolding for Lesson 10.5 (Master), p. 66
Vocabulary/ Symbols	isometric drawing, vertical, diagonal
Workbook	p. 110
Recommended Practice	5, 6 , 7* (Application of Learning), 9 (Communication)
Additional Practice	8 (Knowledge and Understanding), 10, 11 **Extending:** 12, 13 (Problem Solving/Thinking)
Learning Skills	Independent work, Cooperation
Mathematical Processes	Selecting Tools and Computational Strategies, Communicating

*Key Assessment of Learning Question (See chart on p. 36.)

Meeting Individual Needs

Extra Challenge
- Have students make isometric drawings of rectangular objects without using triangle dot paper.

Extra Support
- Provide linking cubes for students as they work through all examples and questions.
- Provide students with linking cubes and triangle dot paper. Have students make a drawing of one cube. Have them add one cube at a time to their drawing to create a layer. Follow the same procedure and have students create a tower. Then have students combine the two activities to create a drawing that has two or three layers.

Math Background

Isometric drawings are a relatively simple first step on the road to true perspective drawing. Because equal lengths on the object are drawn as equal lengths, they are conceptually much simpler. They also offer an early opportunity to begin extending students' thinking toward the concept of an x-y-z coordinate frame. The work students have done in previous lessons in this chapter on recognizing and sketching views will help them to work through the tasks of this lesson. Some students will be able to create correct drawings with reference only to the diagrams; other will continue to require concrete models of the cube structures.

Questions 6, 7, and 8 from Lesson 10.4 can be taken up orally. Have students compare their answers for Questions 9, 10, 11, 12, and 13. Discuss any difficulties that may arise from these questions. Have students sketch the views of shapes from questions with which they had difficulty.

1. Introduction
(Whole Class) ▶ about 5 min

If the Follow-up and Preparation for Next Class in Lesson 10.4 was assigned, have students share their ideas on the importance of being able to recognize and sketch the views of a 3-D figure. Explain that in this lesson, students will be using the three views of a cube structure—top, front, and side—to create another type of 2-D drawing of a 3-D structure. The drawings will be made on triangle dot paper and are called *isometric drawing*. Show students an example of triangle dot paper. Review the difference between a 2-D and 3-D shape.

Sample Discourse

"How many dimensions does a polygon have? What are they"
• *Two, height and width.*

"How many dimensions does a polyhedron have? What are they"
• *Three, height, width, and length.*

"What is another word that can be used for length? It is a word we have been using in this chapter to describe changes in length or height in parts of a structure."
• *Depth.*

Have students turn to Student Book page 364.

2. Teaching and Learning
(Whole Class) ▶ about 15 min

Learn about the Math

With the class, read the problem and central question on Student Book page 364. Review the definition of *isometric drawing* carefully, helping students see that they will be drawing only two types of lines, vertical lines and parallel diagonal lines. One side of a cube will always be represented by the distance between two dots on the dot paper.

Solved Example (Pairs)

Have students work in pairs and read through Miguel's solution in Example 1. Provide linking cubes, triangle dot paper, and rulers and have students reproduce the structure and the diagram, following the explanation in the example. Have pairs discuss the challenges they faced as they completed the task.

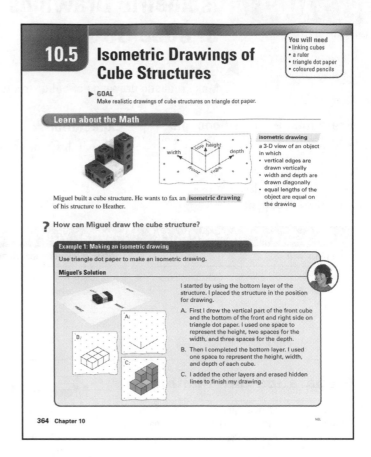

Reflecting

These questions help students to reflect on the steps taken by Miguel to complete his drawing and to consider alternative steps. This reinforces the idea that there can be more than one way to solve a problem.

Answers to Reflecting

1. Miguel placed the bottom layer on a building mat with each straight side of the structure facing one of the views directly.

2. Miguel could have rotated the figure 90 degrees.

3. Yes. For example, Miguel could have set the structure at an angle, so that one of the corners pointed to the front, so he could see the structure as it would appear in an isometric drawing. Then, since one space on the dot paper in any direction represents a side of a cube, he could draw the sides of the cubes that showed in his view. It wouldn't matter if a part of the structure were hidden in the view he chose, because that part would not be shown in the drawing.

3. Consolidation ◖ about 20 min

Solved Example (Individual)

Have students work through Example 2 and duplicate the drawing. Advise students that they will need three shade of colour to shade the drawing, lightest on the top faces of the cubes, medium on the front faces, and darkest on the side faces.

Ⓐ Checking (Individual)

In order to help them with their drawing, have students designate the views of the object.

Answers to Checking

4.

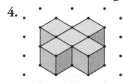

Ⓑ Practising (Individual)

These questions provide students with practice building cube structures and making isometric drawings of the cube structures.

7. If any students need extra support, guide these students and give them a copy of **Scaffolding for Lesson 10.5, Question 7, p. 66.**

Answers to Key Assessment of Learning Question

⛏ 7. (Application of Learning)

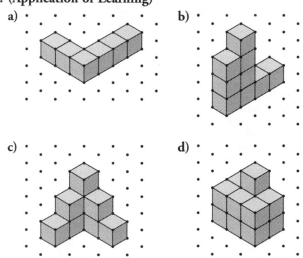

a)

b)

c)

d)

Reflecting

1. Explain how Miguel placed the bottom layer to show a view that he could use to make an isometric drawing.

2. Describe a different way Miguel could have placed the bottom layer to make an isometric drawing.

3. Could Miguel have made an isometric drawing of the structure without first breaking up the layers? Explain.

Example 2: Drawing a cube structure

Make an isometric drawing of this cube structure. Shade your drawing to make it look 3-D.

Solution

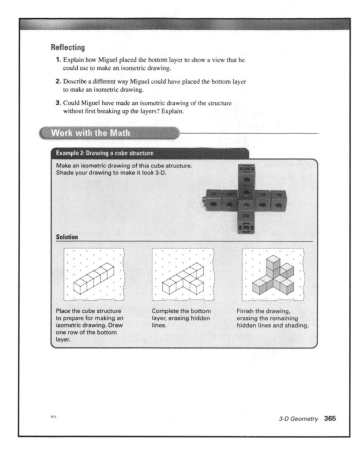

Place the cube structure to prepare for making an isometric drawing. Draw one row of the bottom layer.

Complete the bottom layer, erasing hidden lines.

Finish the drawing, erasing the remaining hidden lines and shading.

NEL

3-D Geometry **365**

Ⓒ Extending (Individual)

These questions allow students to further explore isometric drawings of cube structures from different views. They will help students to look at the complete structure.

Closing (Whole Class)

Near the end of the class, have students summarize what they have learned by asking the following question:

"What are the important steps to completing an isometric drawing of cube structures?"

Follow-Up and Preparation for Next Class

• Have students make an isometric drawing of an object with a simple rectangular shape, such as a brick or book, by first making a linking cube structure of about the same size and shape, drawing the cube structure, and then making any necessary adjustments (for example, rounded corners) to the drawing.

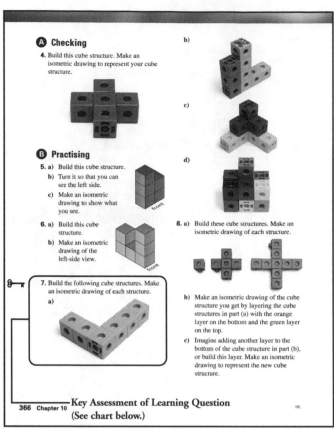

A Checking

4. Build this cube structure. Make an isometric drawing to represent your cube structure.

B Practising

5. a) Build this cube structure.
b) Turn it so that you can see the left side.
c) Make an isometric drawing to show what you see.

6. a) Build this cube structure.
b) Make an isometric drawing of the left-side view.

7. Build the following cube structures. Make an isometric drawing of each structure.
a)

b)

c)

d)

8. a) Build these cube structures. Make an isometric drawing of each structure.

b) Make an isometric drawing of the cube structure you get by layering the cube structures in part (a) with the orange layer on the bottom and the green layer on the top.

c) Imagine adding another layer to the bottom of the cube structure in part (b), or build this layer. Make an isometric drawing to represent the new cube structure.

Key Assessment of Learning Question (See chart below.)

NEL

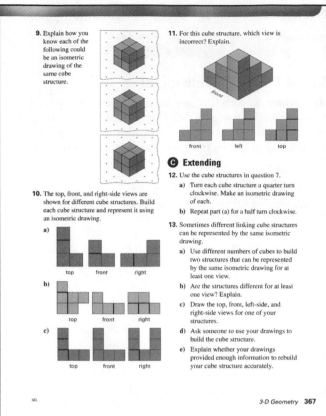

9. Explain how you know each of the following could be an isometric drawing of the same cube structure.

10. The top, front, and right-side views are shown for different cube structures. Build each cube structure and represent it using an isometric drawing.

a)

top   front   right

b)

top   front   right

c)

top   front   right

11. For this cube structure, which view is incorrect? Explain.

front

front   left   top

C Extending

12. Use the cube structures in question 7.
a) Turn each cube structure a quarter turn clockwise. Make an isometric drawing of each.
b) Repeat part (a) for a half turn clockwise.

13. Sometimes different linking cube structures can be represented by the same isometric drawing.
a) Use different numbers of cubes to build two structures that can be represented by the same isometric drawing for at least one view.
b) Are the structures different for at least one view? Explain.
c) Draw the top, front, left-side, and right-side views for one of your structures.
d) Ask someone to use your drawings to build the cube structure.
e) Explain whether your drawings provided enough information to rebuild your cube structure accurately.

NEL   *3-D Geometry* **367**

Assessment of Learning—What to Look for in Student Work...

Assessment Strategy: written answer
Application of Learning

Key Assessment Question 7
• Build the following cube structures.
  Make an isometric drawing of each structure.

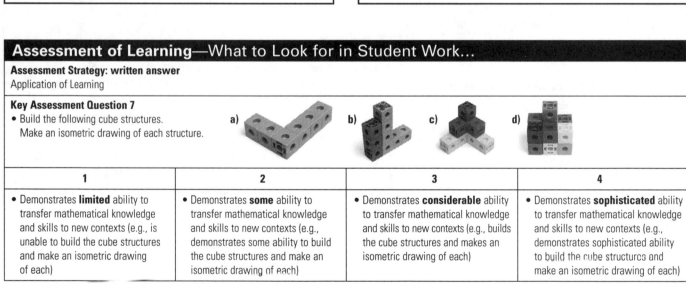

a)   b)   c)   d)

1	2	3	4
• Demonstrates **limited** ability to transfer mathematical knowledge and skills to new contexts (e.g., is unable to build the cube structures and make an isometric drawing of each)	• Demonstrates **some** ability to transfer mathematical knowledge and skills to new contexts (e.g., demonstrates some ability to build the cube structures and make an isometric drawing of each)	• Demonstrates **considerable** ability to transfer mathematical knowledge and skills to new contexts (e.g., builds the cube structures and makes an isometric drawing of each)	• Demonstrates **sophisticated** ability to transfer mathematical knowledge and skills to new contexts (e.g., demonstrates sophisticated ability to build the cube structures and make an isometric drawing of each)

Isometric Drawings of 3-D Objects

▶ **Goal**

Make realistic drawings of 3-D objects on triangle dot paper.

Prerequisite Skills/Concepts

- Create isometric drawings of cube structures.
- Recognize the front, top, and side views of 3-D figures.

Expectations

- identify, through investigation, the minimum side and angle information needed [to describe a unique triangle]

Assessment for Feedback	What You Will See Students Doing...	
Students will	**When students understand**	**If students misunderstand**
• make drawings of 3-D objects on triangle dot paper, working from models and diagrams	• Students will make accurate drawings of 3-D objects on triangle dot paper.	• Some students will have difficulty translating measurements taken from an illustration of a 3-D object into an equivalent number of spaces between dots on the dot paper. Have them round decimal measurements to whole numbers. For prisms, have them measure concrete models and take and use only one measurement for edges that are equal in length. Check that they are drawing only two types of line: vertical and parallel diagonal lines.

Preparation and Planning

Pacing (allow 5 min for previous homework)	**5 min** Introduction **15 min** Teaching and Learning **20 min** Consolidation
Materials	• ruler • 3-D models • *Optional:* linking cubes • 1 cm Triangle Dot Paper, Masters Booklet p. 38
Workbook	pp. 110–111
Recommended Practice	5* (Application of Learning), 6
Additional Practice	7 (Knowledge and Understanding), 8 **Extending:** 9, 10 (Communication), 11, 12, 13 (Problem Solving/Thinking)
Learning Skills	Homework Completion, Class Participation
Mathematical Processes	Connecting, Representing

*Key Assessment of Learning Question (See chart on p. 40.)

Meeting Individual Needs

Extra Challenge

- Students can make isometric drawings of 3-D objects that have rounded edges or unusual shapes, for example, a basketball.
- Students could make isometric drawings of a cluster of objects, for example, a stack of books.

Extra Support

- For Example 1 and Questions 7 and 8, where a 3-D model is not applicable, provide students with linking cubes and a building mat with which to construct a model of the picture. The building mat will ensure students do not confuse the views of the object. Have students create isometric drawings of the views of the object and then combine their work to create one drawing.

Math Background

In Lesson 10.5, students were introduced to the skill of creating a realistic 2-D representation of a cube structure. In this lesson, this learning is extended to working with 3-D shapes that are more challenging in their structure, for example, a hexagonal prism. Students will need to look at the different views of the objects in order to create their drawings.

Dealing with Homework
(Pairs/Whole Class) ▸ about 5 min

Have students compare their answers with a partner. Each partner can choose one question from Lesson 10.5 and explain how they made their drawing. For those questions with which students had difficulty, illustrate the isometric drawing on an overhead or the blackboard. If students were assigned the Follow-Up and Preparation for Next Class activity for Lesson 10.5, have them display their drawings along with the object the drawing represents.

1. Introduction
(Whole Class) ▸ about 5 min

Recall the work done in Lesson 10.5 on the isometric drawing of cube structures. Explain that in this chapter, students will be making isometric drawings of other 3-D objects. Show an example of an object. Ask students what could make the task of drawing this object more challenging than making an isometric drawing of a cube structure.

Sample Discourse

"In the last lesson, we learned to make isometric drawings of cube structures. In this lesson, we will be looking at making isometric drawings of 3-D objects, for example, a knapsack. What could make this task more challenging than making an isometric drawing of a cube structure?"

• *A cube structure consists of straight edges and right angles. This is easier to draw than a 3-D object since a 3-D object does not necessarily have straight edges and right angles.*

Have students turn to Student Book page 368.

2. Teaching and Learning
(Whole Class/Individual) ▸ about 15 min

Learn about the Math

With students, read the central question. Review how, in an isometric drawing, lengths that are equal on the 3-D object are equal in the drawing. Have students measure with a centimetre ruler the two front edges of the Arc de Triomphe in the photograph on Student Book page 368 (one is 5 cm long and the other is 7 cm long). Have them compare these measurements to those in the drawing (the edges are both 7 spaces long). Provide triangle dot paper for students and have them work through prompts A to E individually.

Answers to Learn about the Math

A.–E. Students will follow the step-by-step process to reproduce the drawing on Student Book page 368.

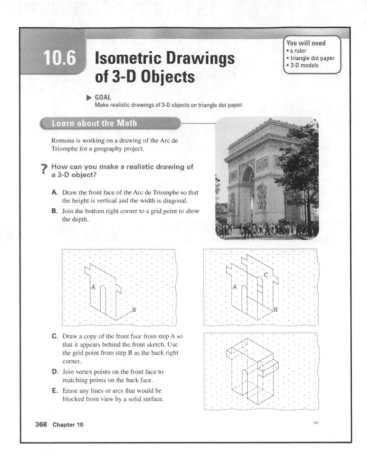

Reflecting

These questions help students to consider the different views of the object and their relationship to each other. This will help students to see the how a sense of depth is achieved in an isometric drawing.

Answers to Reflecting

1. The back face is a copy of the front face because the figure is symmetrical.

2. The front and back faces are parallel 2-D faces, with the dimensions of width and height. When you join matching points on these faces, you add a third dimension, depth.

3. In isometric drawings of both cube structures and of objects, height is shown with vertical lines and width and depth are shown with diagonals. Equal measurements on the structure or object are represented in the drawing by lines of equal length connecting the same number of dots. A cube is made up of straight lines and right angles only, and in an isometric drawing of a cube, the lines are all straight and the angles are all either 60° or 120°. A 3-D object can include curved lines and angles that are not right angles, so in the drawing of the object, there could be curved lines and angles of any size. Also, since all the sides of a cube are equal, you can just make one side equal the space between one dot, so all the lines you draw run through a dot. But a 3-D object could have measurements that are decimals, and then some of the lines in the isometric drawing would be parallel to a row of dots, but not run through the dots.

3. Consolidation ⬧ about 20 min

Solved Examples (Pairs)

Have students read the examples in pairs and discuss which they think is easier. Students may consider Example 2 easier because it uses views of the object.

Ⓐ Checking (Whole Class)

4. For this question, students can look at and measure a 3-D model. If students measure from the photograph, they will obtain a measurement that is a decimal (the dimensions in the picture are 3.5 cm and 2 cm). Have students round to whole numbers. Stronger students can either draw between the dots to show the half unit, or they can convert the measurements to improper fractions and use the numerators of these to get whole number measurements of equivalent proportions.

Answers to Checking

4.

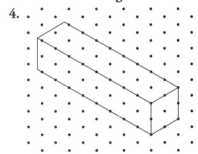

Ⓑ Practising (Individual)

In these questions, students are asked to make isometric drawings of objects that include sharp angles and curved lines, and have measurements that are decimals. Demonstrate to students how to draw curved shapes by first blocking out the shape by drawing a prism or combination of prisms, and then rounding the corners.

5. b) This question is challenging, as an octagon cannot be drawn on triangle dot paper simply by connecting dots. Students will need to draw the horizontal sides of the octagon, which are 1 cm in length and 2 cm apart, and then approximate the positions of the remaining octagon sides before drawing the sides of the prism. They could also treat the photograph as a top view; however, estimation will still be necessary in drawing the base. Alternatively, have students draw a hexagonal prism on the dot paper instead.

6. Explain to students that in each of these diagrams, there is a slanting line that will not run through the dots. This is because slanting lines behave differently in isometric drawings. They should first draw the edges whose measurements are given, then use a ruler to connect up the vertices and draw the remaining lines.

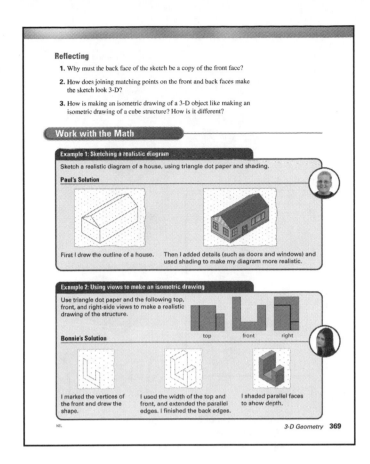

Reflecting

1. Why must the back face of the sketch be a copy of the front face?

2. How does joining matching points on the front and back faces make the sketch look 3-D?

3. How is making an isometric drawing of a 3-D object like making an isometric drawing of a cube structure? How is it different?

Work with the Math

Example 1: Sketching a realistic diagram

Sketch a realistic diagram of a house, using triangle dot paper and shading.

Paul's Solution

First I drew the outline of a house.

Then I added details (such as doors and windows) and used shading to make my diagram more realistic.

Example 2: Using views to make an isometric drawing

Use triangle dot paper and the following top, front, and right-side views to make a realistic drawing of the structure.

top   front   right

Bonnie's Solution

I marked the vertices of the front and drew the shape.

I used the width of the top and front, and extended the parallel edges. I finished the back edges.

I shaded parallel faces to show depth.

NEL   3-D Geometry **369**

7. & 8. Allow students to round measurements to whole numbers if they are having trouble working with measurements that are mixed numbers.

Answers to Key Assessment Question

5. (Application of Learning)

a)   b)

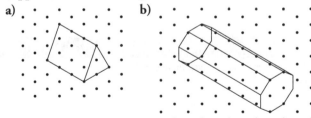

Ⓒ Extending (Individual)

In Questions 9, 10, students are asked to make isometric drawings from different viewpoints. Students are also asked to communicate their understanding of concepts and procedures.

Closing (Whole Class)

In their journals, have students describe a situation in which they might use the technique of isometric drawing in their own artwork.

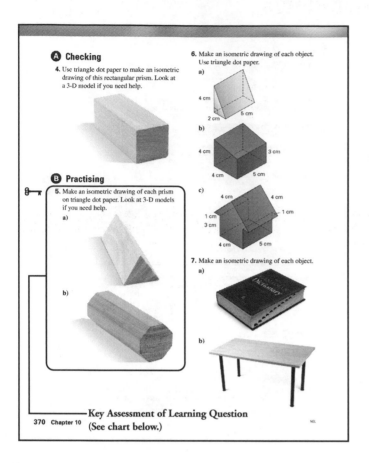

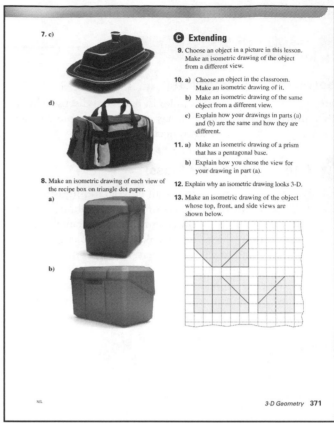

370 | Chapter 10

NEL

NEL

3-D Geometry **371**

Chapter Project Link

In this lesson, students learn to make isometric drawings of 3-D objects on triangle dot paper. They can apply and extend their understanding of this skill in the Chapter Project. (Refer to **Chapter Project: Design a Building p. 70** and the teaching notes on pages 8–9.)

Follow-Up and Preparation for Next Class

- Have students work with a partner. Each one can choose one of the isometric drawings they have made of a 3-D object and give an oral explanation of the process they followed to make the drawing.

Assessment of Learning—What to Look for in Student Work...

Assessment Strategy: written answer
Application of Learning

Key Assessment Question 5
- Make an isometric drawing of each prism on triangle dot paper. Look at 3-D models if you need help.

a)

b)

1	2	3	4
• Demonstrates **limited** ability to transfer mathematical knowledge and skills to new contexts (e.g., is unable to make an isometric drawing of each prism on triangle dot paper)	• Demonstrates **some** ability to transfer mathematical knowledge and skills to new contexts (e.g., demonstrates some ability to make an isometric drawing of each prism on triangle dot paper)	• Demonstrates **considerable** ability to transfer mathematical knowledge and skills to new contexts (e.g., makes an isometric drawing of each prism on triangle dot paper)	• Demonstrates **sophisticated** ability to transfer mathematical knowledge and skills to new contexts (e.g., demonstrates sophisticated ability to make an isometric drawing of each prism on triangle dot paper)

▶ **Goal**

Use mathematical language to describe views of 3-D objects.

Prerequisite Skills/Concepts

- Draw and construct 3-D objects from nets.
- Sketch views of 3-D objects.
- Use mathematical language to describe geometric ideas.

Expectations

- report on [research into real-life] applications of [area] measurements

Assessment for Feedback	What You Will See Students Doing...	
Students will	**When students understand**	**If students misunderstand**
• describe geometric concepts, reasoning, and investigations	• Students will describe geometric concepts, reasoning, and investigations using appropriate math language and covering all points in the Communication Checklist.	• Students may misuse or omit symbols and/or vocabulary in their explanation. Generate a list of the appropriate symbols and vocabulary which students may require to complete an explanation. Summarize the list on chart paper and have students copy the list into their notebooks. • Post the Communication Checklist in the classroom, for example, on chart paper, to which students may refer when writing.

Preparation and Planning

Pacing (allow 5 min for previous homework)	5 min Introduction 15 min Teaching and Learning 20 min Consolidation
Materials	• scissors • tape • linking cubes • *Optional:* overhead projector and transparency of triangle dot paper • *Optional:* photographs of famous buildings • 1 cm Grid Paper, Masters Booklet p. 34 • 2 cm Grid Paper, Masters Booklet p. 36 • 1 cm Triangle Dot Paper, Masters Booklet p. 38
Workbook	p. 112
Recommended Practice	5, 6* (Communication), 7 (Knowledge and Understanding)
Additional Practice	8, 9 (Application of Learning), 10 (Problem Solving/Thinking), 11
Learning Skills	Independent Work, Cooperation
Mathematical Processes	Reasoning and Proving, Communicating

*Key Assessment of Learning Question (See chart on p. 44.)

Meeting Individual Needs

Extra Challenge

- Have students work with a partner. Each partner chooses a photograph of a famous structure, such as the Eiffel Tower, and then draws the three views of it. Each student then uses the Communication Checklist to help them write a paragraph that explains how to create an isometric drawing of their structure. Their partner must try to create an isometric drawing of the structure and identify it.

Extra Support

- Students can work in pairs to choose a polyhedron. One student can write a paragraph explaining how to create a net for the shape and the other could explain how to make an isometric drawing of it. Each partner can check the other's description using the Communication Checklist.

Math Background

Students have learned various ways to represent 3-D shapes with a 2-D drawing. It is important that students learn to explain their thinking in a clear and organized way. They must use the appropriate language and vocabulary in their explanation. This can be difficult for some students. Students may be able to identify a 3-D shape from a 2-D representation and vice versa, but not be able to explain the process followed from one representation to another. Through practice and an emphasis on using appropriate math language and detail, students should find these explanations easier.

Dealing with Homework
(Pairs) ▶ about 5 min

Have students working in pairs compare their answers to Questions 5, 6, 7, and 8 in Lesson 10.6. For those questions with which students had difficulty, illustrate the isometric drawing on the blackboard or on an overhead projector.

1. Introduction
(Whole Class) ▶ about 5 min

Have students refer to Question 8 in the Mid-Chapter Review and explain how they would use these top, front, and left-side views to building a linking-cube structure. Write the explanation in point form on the chalkboard. Then, ask students to put a star beside important details in the explanation, and supply any that are missing; also ask them to underline any math language used, and suggest other terms that could make the explanation clearer. Have students discuss which sketches would be helpful. Also ask students to consider whether the reasoning used to build a model from the views is explained clearly and completely.

2. Teaching and Learning
(Whole Class/Pairs) ▶ about 15 min

Learn about the Math

Have students suggest real-life examples of situations in which it would be important to know the views of a 3-D object (for example, as part of the instructions for assembling a piece of furniture). Together, read the introductory text about Dan's project on Student Book page 372 and the central question. Draw students' attention to the Communication Checklist. Have students working in pairs read Dan's Brochure and Rosa's Questions and discuss the questions Rosa has raised about Dan's description.

Reflecting

Here students consider how they can use a combination of words and drawings to communicate about 3-D models and drawing procedures.

Answers to Reflecting

1. a) yes; For example, if Dan provided a net, he would not need to provide all those steps, because the net would include the precise shapes and measurements.
   b) yes; Showing a front view would make it clear that the pentagon is a regular pentagon. A top or side view would not improve the instructions, because Dan's sketch already provides a general idea of the proportions of the side faces of the prism.
3. Dan used the correct term (pentagonal prism) to describe the shape and also provided a 3-D sketch to show the shape.

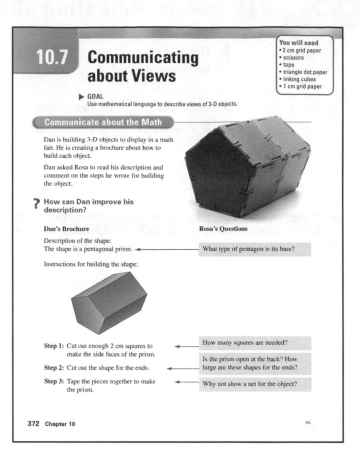

4. Dan did not explain his thinking clearly. He did not explain the reason for taping 2 cm squares instead of just measuring the side faces exactly. He did not explain how many squares you would need, or whether the squares would be taped with any overlap. He left out the important detail that the pentagon has all equal sides. He also omitted the important detail of the size of a side face of the prism, which is needed to know the length of the prism and the length of the sides of the pentagon. His sketch was somewhat helpful, but did not add much information to the description "pentagonal prism." A net or front and side views would have been more useful. He could have used the term regular pentagon.

3. Consolidation ▶ about 20 min

Work with the Math

Solved Example (Individual)

Have students read through the example and follow the instructions to create the isometric drawing.

A Checking (Individual)

This question asks students to think of their own ideas to improve Dan's explanation.

Answers to Checking

4. For example,
Description of the shape: a pentagonal prism with a regular pentagon as its base

Instructions for building the shape:
Step 1: Create a net for the shape:
- Draw a rectangle 10 cm wide and 3 cm long.
- Draw vertical dotted lines dividing the rectangle into five congruent rectangles 2 cm wide and 3 cm long.
- Choose any one of the five rectangles in step 2. On each 2-cm side of the rectangle, draw a regular pentagon with sides 2 cm long that shares that side with the rectangle. Make the side lines where the pentagon joins the rectangle dotted.

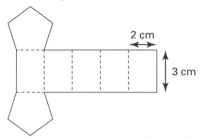

Step 2: Use the net to construct a model of the prism.
- Cut out the net.
- Fold the net at the dotted lines.
- Tape the two 3 cm rectangle edges together.
- Match and tape the edges of each pentagon to the edges of the rectangles, with no overlap.

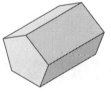

B Practising (Individual)

These questions provide students with practice in writing descriptions and using the Communication Checklist to check their explanations.

Answers to Key Assessment of Learning Question

8→ 6. (Communication)
a) For example,
Description of the structure: a hexagonal prism whose base is the hexagonal shape in the side view shown.
Instructions for building the structure:
Create a net and fold it into the proper shape, as follows:

Drawing the net:
Step 1: Measure the length of each edge of the shape in the side view, and calculate its perimeter.

Step 2: Measure the length of the front view.

Step 3: Draw a rectangle with the same length as the front view and with a width equal to the perimeter of the side view.

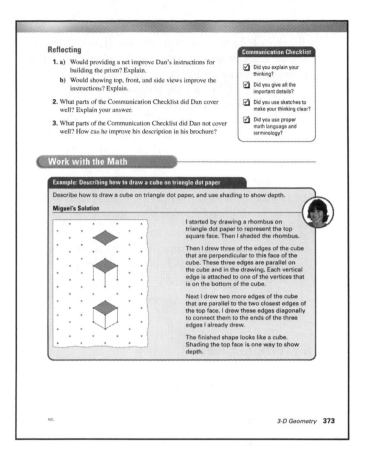

Step 4: Draw lines across the length of your rectangle so that it is divided into several smaller rectangles each with the width of one of the edge-lengths of the side view, matching the right edge of the side view with the bottom of the rectangle and moving clockwise around the hexagon. See the rectangle at the right.

Step 5: On either side of the rectangle that matches the bottom of the hexagon, draw the hexagon so that it shares the bottom edge with the rectangle and so that the edges will all match when the net is folded. See the finished net.

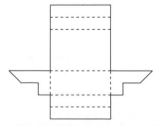

Folding the Net Into the 3-D Object:
Step 1: Fold up the two hexagons.
Step 2: Using the rectangle that shares an edge with the bottom of the hexagon as a base, fold the large rectangle around the hexagons to form the structure.

b) For example, my explanation is very detailed, and the diagrams help to show what the net should look like. My solution is well-organized and I explain my thinking. However, my solution is very long and I think some people might have trouble following so many details. My paragraph will be stronger if I can use fewer words but still make the steps clear. I think I can shorten the explanation if I have readers cut out all the small rectangles individually and then tape them together to form the net.

Revised Paragraph:

Description of the structure: a hexagonal prism whose base is the shape of the side view shown

Instructions for building the structure:
Since the structure is a prism, it has two bases and six side faces that are rectangles each of the same length and with widths the same as the lengths of the sides of the hexagon.

(Answers to Lesson 10.7, Key Assessment of Learning Question **continued on p. 76)**

Closing (Whole Class)

Summarize what students have learned by orally reviewing with them the key components of a well written explanation of a procedure using the Communication Checklist as a reference.

Follow-Up and Preparation for Next Class

• Have students summarize in their journals the key components of a well written explanation as outlined in the Closing discussion.

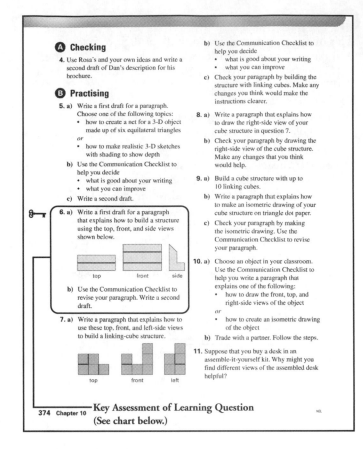

Assessment of Learning—What to Look for in Student Work...

Assessment Strategy: written answer
Communication

Key Assessment Question 6
• **a)** Write a first draft for the paragraph that explains how to build a structure using the top, front, and side views shown below.

• **b)** Use the communication checklist to revise your paragraph. Write a second draft.

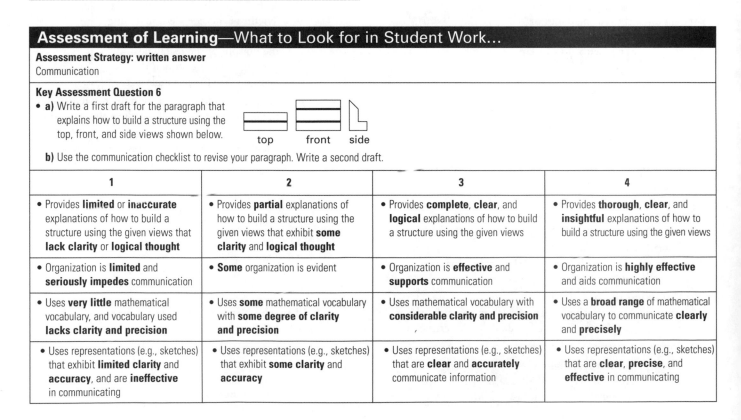

1	2	3	4
• Provides **limited** or **inaccurate** explanations of how to build a structure using the given views that **lack clarity** or **logical thought**	• Provides **partial** explanations of how to build a structure using the given views that exhibit **some clarity** and **logical thought**	• Provides **complete**, **clear**, and **logical** explanations of how to build a structure using the given views	• Provides **thorough**, **clear**, and **insightful** explanations of how to build a structure using the given views
• Organization is **limited** and **seriously impedes** communication	• **Some** organization is evident	• Organization is **effective** and **supports** communication	• Organization is **highly effective** and aids communication
• Uses **very little** mathematical vocabulary, and vocabulary used **lacks clarity and precision**	• Uses **some** mathematical vocabulary with **some degree of clarity and precision**	• Uses mathematical vocabulary with **considerable clarity and precision**	• Uses a **broad range** of mathematical vocabulary to communicate **clearly** and **precisely**
• Uses representations (e.g., sketches) that exhibit **limited clarity** and **accuracy**, and are **ineffective** in communicating	• Uses representations (e.g., sketches) that exhibit **some clarity** and **accuracy**	• Uses representations (e.g., sketches) that are **clear** and **accurately** communicate information	• Uses representations (e.g., sketches) that are **clear**, **precise**, and **effective** in communicating

Math Game: Fishing For Solids

Using the Math Game

Materials: 52 file cards

This game provides practice in identifying 2-D representations of 3-D shapes. Fifty-two file cards are divided into 13 sets of four cards. Each set of cards shows a 3-D shape in four ways, one per card: the name of the shape; a sketch of the shape; the top, front, and right-side views of the shape; and a net of the shape.

Object of the Game

This game is similar to the card game Go Fish. The object of the game is to collect the four cards that represent the same shape and make a set. The one who has the most sets at the end of the game, wins.

When to Play

Students can play this game after Lesson 10.6 when they identify 3-D shapes in the four different ways outlined on the card.

Strategies

Some students may use 3-D models to help them identify the shapes. Other students may look at patterns of shapes in the nets. To match cards, some students may look for shapes that are similar on the net card and the shape card.

Observe

Watch for students who do the following:
• identify the shape on the card regardless of the label
• use the appropriate name of the shape

Discuss

After the game, you might ask students the following:
• What was the most difficult card to use to identify the shape?
• What strategy did you use to identify the shape on the card?

Variations

• Play the game using any combination of two or three cards, for example, the name card and the view card.

Curious Math: Perspective Drawing in Art

Using Curious Math

In this activity, students look at two examples of a 2-D representation of a 3-D shape in a painting. One painting was created in the 1300s and one in the 1500s. Students will see that the later painting gives a better impression of depth.

Answers to Curious Math

1. For example,

Object in woodcut	Polyhedron
hourglass	octagonal prism
sides of ladder	rectangular prisms
nails on ground	square-based pyramids
piece of wood in left corner	octagonal and rectangular prisms
large polyhedron at left side	octahedron?
hammer handle	square-based pyramid, cropped at point
building in background	prism
trim on building	prisms

2. For example, Durer's *Melancholia I* gives a better impression of depth. The Kaufmann *Haggadah* appears more two-dimensional. With *Melancholia I*, it looks like you can reach out and touch the objects and pick them up. You can see a shoreline stretching far into the distance. In *Haggadah*, everything looks very flat. In *Melancholia I*, the width of the hand of the angel and the width of the ladder are about equal. This is like real life, because the ladder is father away and things appear smaller the farther away they are. In *Haggadah*, the front of the table is shorter than the back of the table, even though the back is farther away. Instead of showing depth, Kaufmann just stretched the table and the fireplace into unnatural shapes to try to show perspective.

Answers to Self-Test

1. a) The bottom polyhedron is a cube; the top polyhedron is a square-based pyramid.

b) For example,

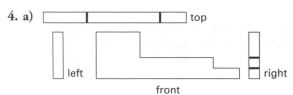

2. B matches all the given views. A matches the back view only. C does not match any views.

3. a)

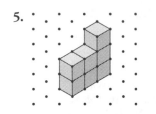

b)

4. a)

top

left

front

right

b)

top   front   left   right

5.

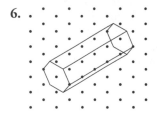

6.

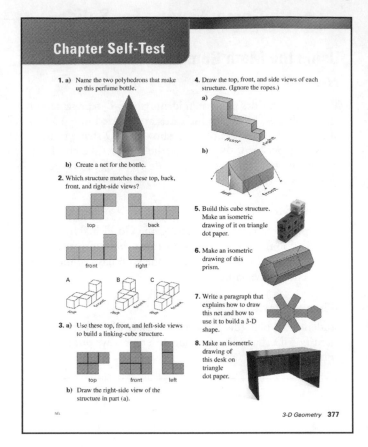

7. For example, to draw the net, first, draw one regular hexagon. Then draw six congruent rectangles using each side of the hexagon as a width. At the open width of one of the rectangles, draw a regular hexagon using the width of the rectangle as a side.

8.

Preparation and Planning

Materials	• Chapter Review—Study Guide (p. 58) • Chapter Review—Frequently Asked Questions (p. 59)

Dealing with Homework
(Whole Class) ▶ about 5 min

Take up Questions 5 and 6 in Lesson 10.7. If the task in Follow-Up and Preparation for Next Class in Lesson 10.7 was assigned, ask students to share their written explanations.

Using the Frequently Asked Questions
(Individual/Groups) ▶ about 10 min

Have students read the Frequently Asked Questions and create a new example for each question in their own notes. Then have students summarize the answers to the Frequently Asked Questions in their own words, as a way of reflecting on the concepts.

Alternately, have students complete **Chapter Review— Frequently Asked Questions p. 58** with their Student Books closed. Compare and discuss students' answers, then compare these answers with those in the Student Book on page 378.

Students can refer to the answers to the Frequently Asked Questions as they work through the Practice Questions.

Using the Practice Questions
(Individual) ▶ about 30 min

Most students will probably complete Questions 1 to 6 in class. Assign the rest for homework.

Assessment of Learning

Use the questions on page 379 of the Student Book to assess the following:
• students' knowledge and understanding of the concepts developed in the chapter
• students' ability to apply learned procedures
• students' ability to solve problems using the concepts developed in the chapter

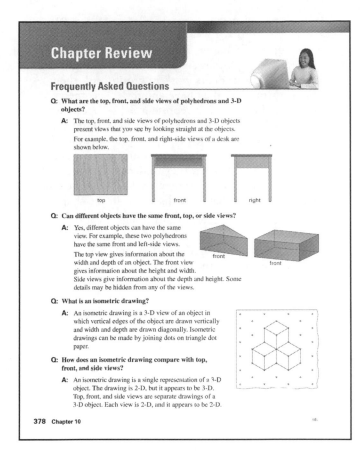

Refer to the **Knowledge and Understanding Rubric, Masters Booklet p. 9**, to get an overall assessment of students' understanding of the concepts. Visit **www.mathK8.nelson.com** and follow the links to Grade 7, Chapter 10 for assessment of learning charts.

Use **Chapter Review—Summary, Masters Booklet p. 22**, to record assessment data.

Follow-Up and Preparation for Next Class

• Provide copies of **Chapter Review—Study Guide p. 57**
to summarize graphically students' understanding of 3-D
geometry. Have students work in groups. Ask them
to brainstorm ideas they have about 3-D geometry
and the methods used to represent 3-D shapes with
a 2-D drawing. Encourage students to consider the
relationships between each type of representation. Have
them read through their list to combine ideas and decide
which best represent what they understand about 3-D
representations. Ensure that they have listed all the types
of representations that were discussed in the chapter.

Alternatively, have students leaf through what they have
learned in this lesson and consider what aspects could
be useful in determining the surface area and volume
of 3-D shapes, which they will explore in Chapter 11.

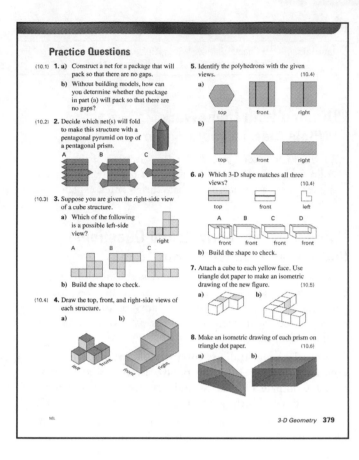

10   Chapter Task

Expectations

- determine, through investigation, using a variety of tools, (e.g. nets, concrete materials dynamic geometry software, Polydrons,) the surface area of right prisms.

Preparation and Planning

Pacing	**5 min** Introducing the Chapter Task **40 min** Using the Chapter Task
Materials	• ruler • scissors • tape • 3-D models • Building Mat (Master) p. 54 • 1 cm Grid Paper, Masters Booklet p. 34 • 2 cm Grid Paper, Masters Booklet p. 36 • 1 cm Triangle Dot Paper, Masters Booklet p. 38 • 2.5 cm Triangle Dot Paper, Masters Booklet p. 39
Enabling Activities	• Building and packing prisms (See Lesson 10.1.) • Building objects from nets (See Lesson 10.2.) • Top, front, and side views of 3-D objects (See Lesson 10.4.) • Isometric drawings of 3-D objects (See Lesson 10.6.) • Communicating about views (See Lesson 10.7.)
Nelson Web Site	• Visit **www.mathK8.nelson.com** and follow the links to *Nelson Mathematics 7*, Chapter 10.

Introducing the Chapter Task
(Whole Class) ⬥ 5 min

Ask students to describe particularly eye-catching chocolate boxes they have seen and explain what aspects of the design made the packaging so effective and appealing. Discuss how package designers have to create packages that not only look good but that also suit the shape and size of what will go in them, have adequate surface area for display and informative text and graphics, and, ideally, pack without gaps.

Using the Chapter Task
(Whole Class/Groups of 4) ⬥ 40 min

Read the opening description of the task on Student Book page 380. Review the instructions and the components of the task: design a box, create a net and use it to make a model, draw views, draw a realistic sketch of the box, and write a proposal that includes both a description of the box and arguments for why the design should win the contest. Have students brainstorm answers to the questions: "What will your gift box look like?" and "What information should be included in the written part of your contest entry?"

A. Each group of four students should agree on a single gift-box design, based on ideas contributed by all students in the group, and record the design concept in a rough sketch that includes measurements. Provide 3-D models for use in conceptualizing and experimenting with design possibilities.

B. Have students in each group divvy up the four components of the task, each taking responsibility for creating one component:
- a description of the gift box design and a convincing argument why the design should be chosen
- a net for the box, and a model of the box made from a copy of the net
- the top, front, and side views of the gift box, suitable to be included in an advertisement (on a copy of the views, students can use dummy text and graphics to indicate how major text and graphics might appear)
- a realistic sketch that can be used in an advertisement (i.e., an isometric drawing, with text and graphics details added as desired)

Within each group, students should compare and critique their work as they proceed, with the goal of producing a coherent and effective contest entry. As students work through the task, observe and/or interview individuals to see how they are interpreting and carrying out the task.

Groups can present their entry to classmates, and students can vote on which is the best design.

Assessing Students' Work

Use the Assessment of Learning chart as a guide for assessing students' work.

Adapting the Task

You can adapt the task in the Student Book to suit the needs of your students. For example:

- Pair stronger math students with those who may require more assistance.
- Have a stronger student illustrate to the rest of the class how to design a gift box by using computer software that includes drawing tools.

Assessment of Learning—What to Look for in Student Work...

Assessment Strategy: Interview/Observation and Product Marketing
Problem Solving/Thinking

	1	2	3	4
Problem Solving/Thinking Prompts A & B Understand the Problem	• shows **limited** understanding of the problem (i.e. is unable to identify relevant information and the relationship between a net, model, and a realistic sketch of a gift box; is unable to restate the problem)	• shows **some** understanding of the problem (i.e. is able to identify some relevant information and the relationship between a net, model, and a realistic sketch of a gift box; may have difficulty restating the problem)	• shows **complete** understanding of the problem (i.e. is able to identify relevant information and the relationship between a net, model, and a realistic sketch of a gift box; is able to restate the problem)	• shows **thorough** understanding of the problem (i.e. is able to differentiate between the relevant and irrelevant information and the relationship between a net, model, and a realistic sketch of a gift box; is able to rephrase the problem)
Prompts A & B Plan: Make a Plan	• shows **little or no evidence** of a plan	• shows **some** evidence of a plan	• shows evidence of an **appropriate** plan	• shows evidence of a **thorough** plan
Prompts A & B Do: Carry Out the Plan	• uses a strategy and **attempts** to solve problem but **does not arrive at an answer**	• carries out the plan **to some extent**, using a strategy, and develops a **partial and/or incorrect solution**	• carries out the plan **effectively** by using an **appropriate** strategy and **solving the problem**	• shows **flexibility** and **insight** when carrying out the plan by **trying** and **adapting**, when necessary, **one or more** strategies to **solve the problem**
Application of Learning Prompts A & B Applying Knowledge and Skill In Familiar Contexts	• demonstrates **limited** ability to apply mathematical knowledge and skills in familiar contexts (i.e. using new learning to design a net model and a realistic design of a gift box)	• demonstrates **some** ability to apply mathematical knowledge and skills in familiar contexts (i.e. using new learning to design a net model and a realistic design of a gift box)	• demonstrates **considerable** ability to apply mathematical knowledge and skills in familiar contexts (i.e. using new learning to design a net model and a realistic design of a gift box)	• demonstrates **sophisticated** ability to apply mathematical knowledge and skills in familiar contexts (i.e. using new learning to design a net model and a realistic design of a gift box)
Communication Prompt B Explanation and Justification of Mathematical Concepts, Procedures, and Problem Solving	• provides **limited or inaccurate** explanations/justifications that lack clarity or logical thought, using minimal words, pictures, symbols, and/or numbers of the appropriate method needed to prepare the contest entry of a description, a net, a model, and a realistic sketch of the gift box	• provides **partial** explanations/justifications that exhibit some clarity or logical thought, using simple words, pictures, symbols, and/or numbers of the appropriate method needed to prepare the contest entry of a description, a net, a model, and a realistic sketch of the gift box	• provides **complete, clear and logical** explanations/justifications using appropriate words, pictures, symbols, and/or numbers of the appropriate method needed to prepare the contest entry of a description, a net, a model, and a realistic sketch of the gift box	• provides **thorough, clear and insightful** explanations/justifications using a range of words, pictures, symbols, and/or numbers of the appropriate method needed to prepare the contest entry of a description, a net, a model, and a realistic sketch of the gift box
Prompt B Organization of Material (written, spoken or drawn)	• organization is **limited and seriously impedes** communication	• **some** organization is evident	• organization is **effective** and supports communication	• organization is **highly effective and aids** communication
Prompt B Organization of Material (written, spoken or drawn)	• uses representations that exhibit **limited** clarity and **accuracy**, and are **ineffective** in communicating	• uses representations that exhibit **some clarity** and **accuracy**	• uses representations that **clearly** and **accurately** communicate information	• uses representations that are **clear, precise,** and **effective** in communicating

Family Newsletter

Dear Parent/Caregiver:

Over the next three weeks, your child will be learning about 3-D geometry and how to draw 2-D representations of 3-D shapes.

To reinforce the concepts your child is learning at school, you and your child can work on some at-home activities such as these:

- Look in your community for buildings that use an interesting combination of 3-D geometric shapes, or find images of buildings famous for their design in books and magazines or on the Internet.
- Draw a mini-net to scale for a room in your home, and construct a model using the net.
- Build shapes with blocks and draw different views.
- Sketch a view from the ceiling of the furniture in a room in your home.
- Draw another view of a building or object in a photograph.
- Using triangle dot paper, make isometric drawings of household objects.

You may want to visit the Nelson Web site at **www.mathK8.nelson.com** for more suggestions to help your child learn mathematics and develop a positive attitude toward learning mathematics. As well, you can check the Nelson Web site for links to other Web sites that provide online tutorials, math problems, brainteasers, and challenges.

Nets of Prisms (page 1)

Lesson 10.1: Building and Packing Prisms

STUDENT BOOK PAGE 348

Nets of Prisms (page 2)

Lesson 10.1: Building and Packing Prisms

STUDENT BOOK PAGE 348

Building Mat

Lessons 10.3: Top, Front, and Side Views of Cube Structures

Lessons 10.4: Top, Front, and Side Views of 3-D Objects

STUDENT BOOK PAGES 354–357, 360–363

BACK

LEFT

RIGHT

FRONT

Name: _____ Date: _____

Mid-Chapter Review—Study Guide

STUDENT BOOK PAGES 358–359

A. What two ways have you used to represent a 3-D object?

- _____

- _____

B. What is a net?

_____

_____

_____

C. When drawing a net, how do you show an edge that will be folded?

_____

_____

_____

Diagram

D. What different views can represent a cube structure?

- _____

- _____

- _____

E. How is a change in depth shown on a view?

_____

_____

_____

Diagram

Mid-Chapter Review—Frequently Asked Questions

STUDENT BOOK PAGE 358

Q: How can you predict whether congruent prisms will fill a space without any gaps?

A: _____

_____

_____

_____

Q: When and how can you combine two different nets to make a single net for a shape?

A: _____

_____

_____

_____

Q: What are the top, front, and side views of a cube structure?

A: _____

_____

_____

_____

Q: Do three views of a cube structure always provide enough information to build the cube structure?

A: _____

_____

_____

_____

Chapter Review—Study Guide

STUDENT BOOK PAGES 378–379

A. Copy and complete the following concept charts for 2-D representations of 3-D models, using a 3-D shape to draw examples.

Nets		
Written explanation	Example	Methods used to make nets

Views of 3-D Objects		
Written explanation	Example	Methods used to draw views

Isometric drawings of 3-D Objects		
Written explanation	Example	Methods used to create isometric drawings

Name: ______________________ Date: ______________________

Chapter Review—Frequently Asked Questions

STUDENT BOOK PAGE 378

Q: What are the top, front, and side views of polyhedrons and 3-D objects?

A: ______________________

Q: Can different objects have the same front, top, or side views?

A: ______________________

Q: What is an isometric drawing?

A: ______________________

Q: How does an isometric drawing compare with top, front, and side views?

A: ______________________

Scaffolding for Getting Started Activity (page 1)

STUDENT BOOK PAGE 346

B. Visualize folding the nets on the next page into cubes. On each net, lightly mark the faces that you predict will be opposite each other. Use a 3-D model of a cube to help you determine which faces to mark:
  - Lightly mark opposite faces on the 3-D model.
  - Set the 3-D model on a square in the net.
  - Roll the model around the net to determine which faces will be opposite faces.

C. Cut out the nets. Fold the cubes to check that you have marked opposite faces correctly. Unfold the cubes and colour the faces of the net so that when the net is a cube, opposite faces will be the same colour.

D. Construct the cubes.

E. How many faces does a cube have? _____

How many pairs of faces does a cube have? _____

Can opposite faces on a cube touch along any edge? _____

Which net was easiest to use for matching the colours of opposite faces?

_____

What do you think made it easiest?

_____

_____

_____

_____

F. Design a different net for a cube. Use grid paper. Repeat parts B to D for your net.

Scaffolding for Getting Started Activity (page 2)

STUDENT BOOK PAGE 346

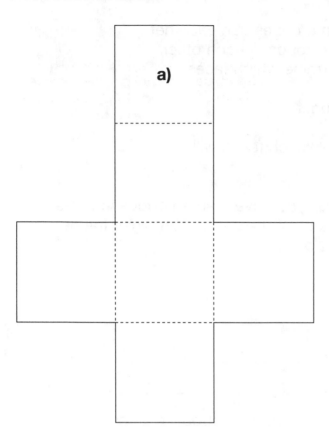

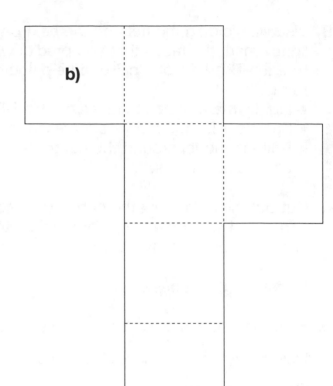

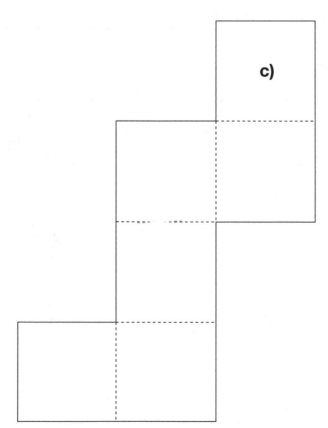

Scaffolding for Do You Remember? Questions 1–11 (page 1)

STUDENT BOOK PAGE 347

1. Sketch an example of each polygon. Mark any sides that must be equal.

   a) isosceles triangle   **b)** equilateral triangle

   c) quadrilateral   **d)** pentagon

   e) hexagon   **f)** octagon

   polygon: A closed 2-D shape with sides made from straight line segments

   isosceles: In a triangle, having 2 sides equal in length

   equilateral: In a triangle, having all sides equal in length

   quadrilateral: A polygon with 4 straight sides

   pentagon: A polygon with 5 sides

   hexagon: A polygon with 6 sides

   octagon: A polygon with 8 sides

2. State whether each shape is a prism or a pyramid.

   a)

   _____

   b)

   _____

   c)

   _____

   d)

   _____

   e)

   _____

   f)

   _____

   polyhedron: A 3-D shape that is formed by polygons

   prism: A polyhedron with opposite congruent bases; the other faces are parallelograms.

   pyramid: A polyhedron with a polygon for a base; the other faces are triangles that meet at a single vertex

3. Name each base and each prism.

	Base	Prism
a) 		
b)		
c)		

   A prism is named according to the polygon that is its base.

Scaffolding for Do You Remember? Questions 1–11 (page 2)

STUDENT BOOK PAGE 347

4. Name each base and each pyramid.

	Base	Pyramid
a) 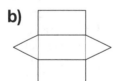		
b) 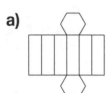		
c) 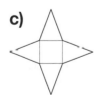		

A pyramid is also named according to the polygon that is its base.

tetrahedron: A 3-D shape with 4 faces that are polygons

5. Which pyramid in question 4 is a tetrahedron? _____

6. & 7. Match each net with a polyhedron, and each polyhedron with a name on the list.

a)

A.

- triangular pyramid
- hexagonal prism
- triangular prism
- square-based pyramid
- hexagonal pyramid
- pentagonal prism
- octagonal prism
- pentagonal pyramid

b)

B.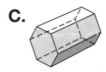

c)

C.

D.

Scaffolding for Do You Remember? Questions 1–11 (page 3)

STUDENT BOOK PAGE 347

8.–10. Complete this table and the questions below it, then answer questions 8, 9, and 10. Use 3-D models to help you.

Polyhedron	Faces	Edges	Vertices
Triangular pyramid			
Triangular prism			
Square-based pyramid			
Square-based prism			
Pentagonal pyramid			
Pentagonal prism			
Hexagonal pyramid			
Hexagonal prism			

face: A polygon that forms a flat surface of a polyhedron

edge: The line segment formed where 2 faces meet on a polyhedron

vertex (plural is **vertices**): The point where 2 or more edges meet

Which polygon (2-D shape) has the least number of sides? _____

Which polyhedron (3-D shape) has the least number of faces, edges, and vertices? _____

What is the name for any 3-D shape with four faces that are polygons?

_____

   i. What is the least number of faces that a polyhedron can have? _____

   ii. What is the least number of edges that a polyhedron can have? _____

   iii. What is the least number of vertices that a polyhedron can have? _____

11. Explain the difference between a polygon and a polyhedron. _____

_____

_____

_____

_____

Scaffolding for Lesson 10.3, Question 6

STUDENT BOOK PAGE 356

6. a) Build this structure with linking cubes and place it on your building mat.

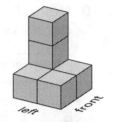

left   front

b) Follow the steps below to draw the three views of the structure.

Step 1: Build the first layer of the structure. Draw the front, top, and left side view of this layer.

FRONT
Bring your eye level with the structure and turn the mat to see the front view.

LEFT SIDE
Turn the mat so that you are looking directly at the left-side view.

TOP
Look directly down on the structure to see the top view.

Step 2: Add the second layer to your structure.
On the above views, make a thick black line where there is a change in depth.
Draw the second layer on the above front, top, and left-side views.

Step 3: Add the third layer to your structure.
On the above views, make a thick black line where there is a change in depth.
Draw the third layer on the above front, top and left-side views.

Scaffolding for Lesson 10.5, Question 7 b), c), d)

STUDENT BOOK PAGE 366

7. Build the following cube structures.
Make an isometric drawing of each structure.

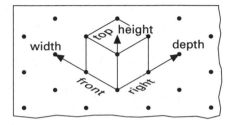

An **isometric drawing** is a 3-D view in which:

- vertical edges are drawn vertically
- width and depth are drawn diagonally
- equal lengths of the object are equal on the drawing

You can follow these steps:

Step 1: Place the structure on a building mat so that its width and depth run diagonally.

Step 2: Build the first layer of the structure. Make an isometric drawing of the first layer on triangle dot paper. Use one space to represent the height, width, and depth of each cube.

Step 3: Add the second layer to the structure. Draw the second layer. Erase hidden lines.

Step 4: Add the third layer to the structure. Draw the third layer. Erase the remaining hidden lines. Shade your drawing to make it look 3-D.

Chapter 10 Test (page 1)

1. a) Name the two polyhedrons that make up this perfume bottle.

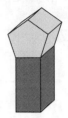

_____

_____

b) Create a net for the bottle.

2. Which structure matches which of these top, back, front, and right-side views?

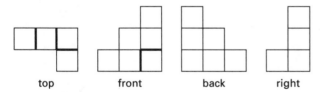

| top | front | back | right |

A.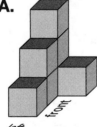

left front

B.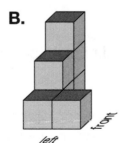

left front

C.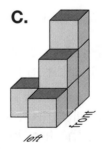

left front

_____

_____

_____

_____

Chapter 10 Test (page 2)

3. a) Use these top, front, and right-side views to build a linking-cube structure.

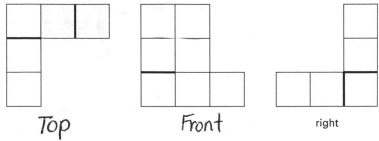

Top   Front   right

b) Draw the left-side view of the structure in part (a).

4. Draw the top, front, and side views of each structure. (both right and left side views)

a)

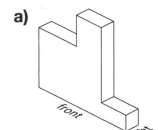

front   right

b)

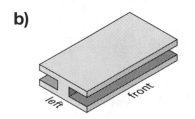

left   front

Chapter 10 Test (page 3)

5. Build this cube structure. Make an isometric drawing of it on triangle dot paper.

6. Make an isometric drawing of this prism.

7. Write a paragraph that explains how to draw this net and how to use it to build a 3-D shape.

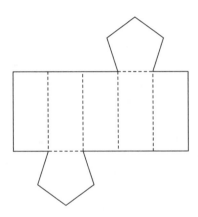

_____

_____

_____

_____

_____

_____

_____

_____

8. Make an isometric drawing of this table on triangle dot paper.

Chapter 10 Task

STUDENT BOOK PAGE 380

A. Design and construct a fancy, unique gift box for chocolates that will be appealing and attractive to customers.

B. i) Describe your gift box.

Explain why your design should be chosen.

ii) Design and draw a net for your gift box.
Make a copy of the net and use it to construct a model of your gift box.

iii) Draw the top, front, and side views of your gift box. The drawings should be suitable to be included in an advertisement.

iv) Make a realistic sketch of your gift box that can be used in an advertisement.

Task Checklist

☐ Is your description clear?

☐ Did you use correct math language?

☐ Did you include all the required diagrams and sketches?

☐ Did you draw your diagrams accurately?

☐ Did you include a carefully constructed model?

Chapter Project: Design a Building

Architects use their knowledge of line and shape to create beautiful buildings that suit their function. Use your knowledge of 3-D geometry to design a building.

Lesson 10.1: Building and Packing Prisms

A. Describe the function for which your building will be designed and any special features it will need to have.

B. Create a design using 2–4 different prisms (use 3-D models or make rough sketches). Make sure each section of the building is connected. Describe what each section will be used for.

C. Draw the footprint, or perimeter, of your building.

D. Draw a net for each prism (make copies of a net you will use more than once). Build the prisms. Connect them to make a 3-D model of your building.

Lesson 10.2: Building Objects from Nets

E. Combine the nets of two or more of your prisms to simplify your model. Or, make alterations to one of your nets to create a section of your building that is not a prism (for example, add a pointed roof).

Lesson 10.4: Top, Front, and Side Views of 3-D Objects

F. Use your models to draw the top, front, back, and side views of your building.

Lesson 10.6: Isometric Drawings of 3-D Objects

G. Draw your building on triangle dot paper. Add details such as doors and windows.

Examples

B.

C.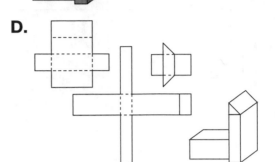

D.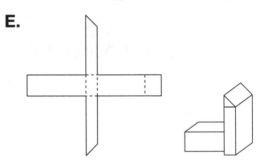

E.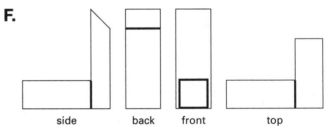

F.

side   back   front   top

G.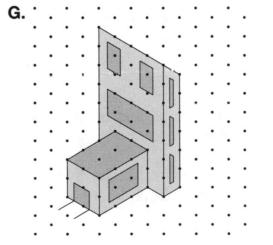

Answers for Chapter 10 Masters

Scaffolding Answers

Scaffolding for Getting Started Activity p. 59

B. a)

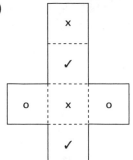

b)

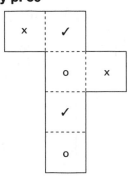

c)

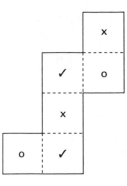

C. a)

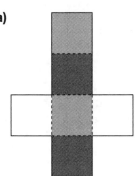

b)

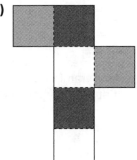

c)

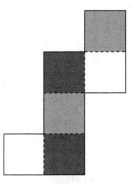

E. six faces; three pairs of faces; opposite faces cannot touch along any edge. For example, the net in part a) was easiest. It was the easiest because each pair of opposite faces had one face in between them on the net.

F. For example,

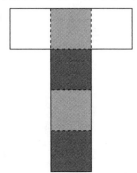

Scaffolding for Do You Remember? pp. 61–63

1. a)   **b)**   **c)**   **d)**   **e)**   **f)**

2. a) pyramid   **b)** prism   **c)** neither   **d)** prism   **e)** neither   **f)** prism

3. a) pentagon, pentagonal prism
   b) octagon, octagonal prism
   c) rectangle, rectangular prism

4. **a)** hexagon, hexagonal pyramid

   b) triangle, triangular pyramid

   c) pentagon, pentagonal pyramid

5. The pyramid in part b) is a tetrahedron.

6. & 7 Net a) matches C, a hexagonal prism; net b) matches A, triangular prism; net c) matches D, a square-based pyramid; B is a pentagonal pyramid.

8.–10.

Polyhedron	Faces	Edges	Vertices
Triangular pyramid	4	6	4
Triangular prism	5	9	6
Square-based pyramid	5	8	5
Square-based prism	6	12	8
Pentagonal pyramid	6	10	6
Pentagonal prism	7	15	10
Hexagonal pyramid	7	12	7
Hexagonal prism	8	18	12

A triangle has the least number of sides. A triangular pyramid has the least number of faces, edges, and vertices. A 3-D shape with four faces that are polygons is called a tetrahedron.

   i. 4 faces

   ii. 6 edges

   iii 4 vertices

11. A polygon is a 2-D closed shape whose sides are straight lines. A polyhedron is a 3-D figure with faces that are polygons.

Scaffolding for Lesson 10.3, Question 6, p. 64

   6. b) Step 1:

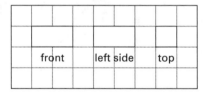

   Step 2:

   Step 3:

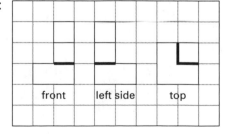

Scaffolding for Lesson 10.5, Question 7 b), c), d), p. 65

7. b) 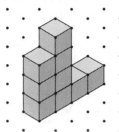 **c)**   **d)**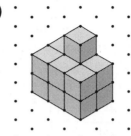

Chapter Test Master, pp. 66–68

1. **a)** The bottom polyhedron is a rectangular or square-based prism; the top polyhedron is a pentagonal prism.

    b) For example,

    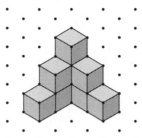

2. A matches all the given views. B matches at the back only. C does not match any views.

3. **a)** 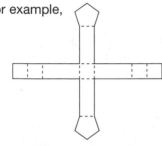   **b)**

    left

4. **a)**

    top   front   right left

    b)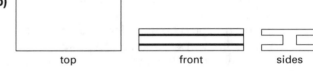

    top   front   sides

5.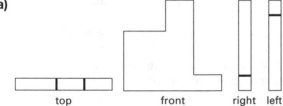

6.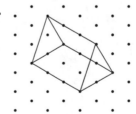

7. For example, to draw the net, first draw five congruent rectangles side by side, attached along the longer side of the rectangle. Draw one regular pentagon with one side shared with the open top side of the second rectangle from the right. Draw a congruent pentagon with one side shared with the open bottom side of the second rectangle from the left.

8.

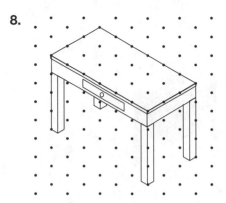

Chapter 10 Task Master, p. 69

A. Answers will vary greatly depending on the gift-box design created.

B. For example,

Description: The gift box has a rectangular prism base (length 21 cm, width 15 cm, height 4 cm) with a lid made up of three congruent prisms, with an isosceles triangle base (the triangle is 2 cm high and 7 cm at the base) and sides 15 cm long.

Why this design should be chosen:

- The design is unique. There is no other chocolate box that is shaped like this.
- The triangular prisms on the lid are eye-catching. They look like mountains, and some of the best milk chocolate comes from Switzerland, a land of mountains, so it will make people think of quality chocolate.
- There is lots of surface space on this box for the name of the chocolates and attractive graphic design. The lid of the box has a base so that when you open the box there can be a picture of the types of chocolates.
- The box will hold two layers of chocolates, which is ideal; too many layers means people can mess up the chocolates looking for the one they want; only one layer means too much packaging for the amount of chocolates, it could look like you were trying to make it seem like there were more chocolates than there are, and also people don't like to buy things that have too much waste packaging.
- This design could be used for different sizes of boxes in a series. For example, a smaller gift box could have two mountains and one layer of chocolates.
- This box will pack in cartons without gaps, because the shape of the sides tessellates. You need to pack the chocolate boxes flat, or the chocolate could get broken.

Net and model:

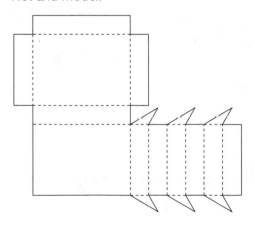
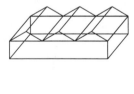

Views:

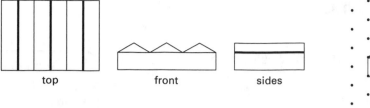

top   front   sides

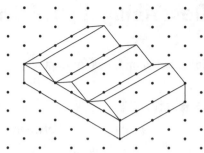

Answers to Lesson 7, Key Assessment of Learning Question (continued from p. 44)

Step 1: Draw two congruent hexagons in the same shape as the side view.

Step 2: Measure the length of each side of the hexagon.

Step 3: Draw and cut out six rectangles from a piece of paper, all with the same length, and with widths matching the six sides of the hexagon.

Step 4: Arrange the rectangles in the same order as the sides of the hexagon, so that they will each match with the proper sides of the hexagon when folded. Tape the rectangles together.

Step 5: Find the rectangle that matches the bottom side of the hexagon and tape the hexagons to either end of it, oriented so that all the sides will match when the net is folded.

Step 6: Construct the structure by folding and taping the net.

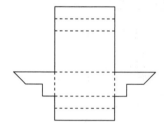

Describing Right Prisms

GOAL   Investigate between faces for right prisms, and identify right prisms.

Explore the Math

Miguel thinks there is a relationship between angle measures at **vertices** of **right prisms** and which **faces** are perpendicular.

> **? How do angle measures show which faces of a right prism are perpendicular?**

A. How can you identify a right prism by looking at the base? Give two examples.

B. Measure each angle on a side face of a triangular prism. What are the angle measures? What are the angle measures at the vertices of the other side faces? What polygon is each side face? Is each side face perpendicular to the base?

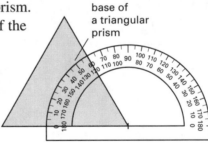

side face of a triangular prism

C. Measure each angle on the base of the triangular prism. What are the angle measures? Are the side faces of the prism perpendicular to each other?

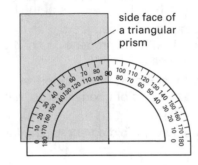

base of a triangular prism

D. Repeat steps B and C for a rectangular prism.

E. Repeat steps B and C for three other right prisms. Use 3-D models and right prisms constructed by stacking pattern blocks.

Reflecting

1. a) How do the angle measures on the side faces of a right prism show whether the side faces are rectangles?

  b) How do the angle measures on the side faces of a right prism show whether the base is perpendicular to the base?

2. What do your answers in question 1 show about right prisms?

3. What does your investigation show about whether faces of right prisms are perpendicular to each other?

You will need
• 3-D models
• pattern blocks
• a protractor

right prism
a prism with two congruent polygons joined by rectangular sides

Chapter 10 Expectations and Answers

10A Describing Right Prisms (Exploration)

Expectations

- [construct related lines, and] classify [triangles, quadrilaterals, and] prisms
- investigate, using concrete materials, the angles between the faces of a prism, and identify right prisms

Answers

  A. The type of prism depends on the shape of the base. A triangular prism has a triangular base. A rectangular prism has a rectangular base.

  B. 90° for all angles of each side face; rectangle; yes

  C. 60° for all angles of the base; no

  D. For a side face: 90° for all angles of each side face; rectangle, yes
     For the base: 90° for all angles of the base; yes

  E. For example, a prism made with tan rhombus pattern blocks

     For a side face: 90° for all angles of each side face; rectangle, yes

     For the base: 30°, 150°, 30°, 150°, parallelogram or rhombus, no

     For example, a prism made with blue rhombus pattern blocks

     For a side face: 90° for all angles of each side face; rectangle, yes

     For the base: 60°, 120°, 60°, 120°, parallelogram or rhombus, no

     For example, a prism made with red trapezoid pattern blocks

     For a side face: 90° for all angles of each side face; rectangle, yes

     For the base: 60°, 120°, 120°, 60°, trapezoid, no

  1. **a)** The angle measures are 90° so the side faces are rectangular faces.

     b) The angle measures are 90° so the side faces are perpendicular to the base.

  2. If the angle measures on the base are 90°, the side faces are perpendicular to each other. If the angle measures on the base are not 90°, the side faces are not perpendicular to each other.

  3. The side faces of right prisms are rectangles that are perpendicular to the base. For some right prisms, the side faces are perpendicular to each other, but for most right prisms the side faces not perpendicular to each other.